A la mémoire de toutes mes voix
chères qui se sont tues.

"The wind brings
Fallen leaves enough
To make a fire." [1]

CONTENTS

Part One	MY STORY

Part Two	CLEARING OUT THE JUNK ON ALL LEVELS

ACKNOWLEDGEMENTS

THIS BOOK would never have seen the light of day without the help, support and generosity of many people so here is my opportunity to give them all a big 'thank you' from the bottom of my heart:

First and foremost mon Ian chéri, my 'long-suffering husband', my soul mate, for his great resilience throughout our years together, for accompanying me on this journey, for his support and love without which I would not be here today.

To Graham Milne, for being such a great teacher, for having the courage to stand by me, for being such an inspiration when I was lost.

To Ann, for being the first one to read the manuscript, as it was then, and still believe that it was worth publishing.

To David Hamilton, for writing the foreword of this book and for being such a guiding light to us all.

To Cherie Calbom, for allowing me to reproduce the diet from *Juicing for Life* (Avery publishers) virtually unchanged and Pat Thomas, for allowing me to quote extensively from her articles and her book *Cleaning Yourself to Death* (Newleaf publishers).

To Bernie Siegel, for his understanding of human nature of for being so generous to me.

To Rudolf Breuss, for writing such a detailed description of his approach to this kind of disease and for the look in his eyes that somehow told me all I needed to know.

To my lucky stars, for selecting Dr. Patricia Clarke as my consultant and to Dr. Clarke herself for daring to be a human being first and a consultant second.

To Dr. Ian McGlinchey, for his cheerfulness and for taking the trouble to choose the best scan pictures, so they could be included in this book, and thanks for the title too!

To my many friends who supported me, made me laugh and kicked my backside when I needed it and, in particular: Monique for getting on a plane and managing to be here for me when I was in the grip of tremendous fear; Herb and Elly, our dear friends from the United States who took the first available plane to come and offer their support; Meg for letting me drag her up the hill now and again; Shona 'the Rottweiler woman' for her repeated naggings, pestering and questionings about when this book would be finished; Christine for encouraging me to eat more healthily and introducing me to organic vegetables; Denise for her friend-ship and for nudging me in the right direction, when my natural laziness would have otherwise made me miss out on great workshops or opportunities to learn; To Mhairi Mcleod, for reading the final version and her enthusiastic feedback; To Bàra, for being a tower of strength and a great support when I needed her.

To Sue Biazotti for her unquenchable enthusiasm regarding this venture, for spending a whole afternoon taking four hundred photos of my face, for not despairing.

To Bernard Chandler, 'Bernie', for daring to take on this angst-ridden control freak and still managing to come up with a great design for this book. Genius!

Finally, to my family for not putting pressure on me in spite of their own reservations, for allowing me to do it my way. Respect.

Love and thanks to you all.

Cathie Grout
26/10/2009

"RABBITS DON'T GET LYMPHOMA!"

FOREWORD

by David R. Hamilton PhD

THE MIND has a powerful effect upon the body and even more so when we direct it in a positive way. I have been researching the mind for 25 years now. As a 12-year-old, the first book I ever read was called *The Magic Power of the Mind*.

As an adult following a PhD in chemistry, I spent four years as a scientist in the pharmaceutical industry where I was exposed to the power of the placebo effect. People in medical trials recover from illness and disease mostly because they believe that they are receiving a drug when actually they receive a dummy drug – a placebo. The placebo effect has been known for hundreds of years but the study of the mind's ability to affect the body has come a long way since early studies of the placebo effect.

Current research in the field of neuroscience has revealed that every thought affects the microscopic structure of the brain. The brain is not a lump of hardwired material, as was once thought, but an ever-changing organic bio-computer that evolves to the tune of our thinking. Thoughts and emotions also produce chemicals that affect cells all throughout the body and even influence us at the genetic level. Thus, the entire biology of the body dances to the tune of the mind. And you are the composer of the tune.

Thoughts directed in a healing way impact the condition of the body. For example, research has now revealed that when you imagine moving a part of your body, the area of the brain that governs that part is stimulated and so also is the body part. Recent discoveries in rehabilitation from stroke, Parkinson's disease and from spinal cord injury, for instance, has shown that visualisation of movements stimulates the brain area that controls each area a patient imagines moving and also sends impulses to the muscles. Thus, movement improves. And amazingly, in the case of stroke, damaged brain areas begin to regenerate.

But the mind can be used to heal much more than this, as you will soon learn. A thought of any part of the body affects that part. Healing thoughts or healing affirmations, therefore, directed to any part of the body, or addressing any condition, ultimately affect that part or the condition.

This wonderful, empowering, book demonstrates just how powerful the mind can be - through the use of visualisation and affirmation - to affect the state of such a serious condition as non-Hodgkin's lymphoma.

I am inspired by Cathie and I hope that her story inspires you too. I hope that you take away something extremely positive from this book. Perhaps it is something that can help you in your own life, or maybe it is some advice that you can pass on to someone else in need. I am sure that it can make a real difference.

David R. Hamilton PhD

INTRODUCTION

DURING THE LAST TWENTY YEARS, the incidence of non-Hodgkin's lymphoma has increased by approximately 73 percent. It now accounts for three percent of all cancers. This once rare disease is not so rare anymore and neither fame nor wealth protects you from it or influences the outcome. Jackie Onassis and King Hussein of Jordan did not survive it.

Then nearly eleven years ago I too was diagnosed with this condition. When I decided to find out if anyone had ever written something that I could understand about this form of cancer I was disappointed, to put it mildly. There were indeed a few books written by cancer survivors, but none were about this 'lymphoma'. I did find out, however, that this type of cancer seemed to affect mostly men.

Ah, yes, that would be right. Trust me to get something weird like that.

Actually, by a twist of fate, the very weirdness of this disease was going to play an unexpected part in my ability to tackle it.

Cancer was an old familiar companion to me, almost a member of my family. My aunt and uncle had died of it within two years of each other. My dad, their brother, had also been diagnosed with prostate cancer in his late seventies. He died aged 84. For my aunt and uncle who were in their early 60s and late 50s respectively when diagnosed, time had been of the essence and treatment had consisted of surgery, radiotherapy and chemotherapy. My dad, however, followed a slightly different route because of his age, and because his type of cancer was not supposed to evolve rapidly. He was mostly treated with hormone injections and, a couple of years before he died, radiotherapy. Towards the end, he also had to endure palliative surgery to try and help him to pass urine. This failed miserably and only made his last few weeks more painful.

After my diagnosis, and because of the pattern in my family history, I fully expected to be told that there was not a moment to lose and that treatment would commence immediately. This is where my journey began - when the proposed treatment was explained to me.

I never spent any time wondering 'why me' or 'why did I have to have cancer'. My family seemed to have a great ability for developing this disease! As my relatives had before me, I had resigned myself to having chemotherapy and probably radiotherapy. That was not the problem. My problem, and also my incredible luck, was that treatment could **not** start until my lymphoma was correctly identified. My consultant explained that my treatment would be determined by the type of lymphoma I had and the stage it was at. Apparently it was quite tricky to reach a correct diagnosis. It required two teams to work separately and compare their findings. I was told that the whole procedure usually took about five weeks. Whilst I was strangely flattered that **my** cancer was going to require **two** teams, the thought of no treatment for five weeks filled me with terror. I did not know then that those five weeks were a gift and that I would use them so productively that my attitude towards the proposed treatment would change radically.

Sometimes people diagnosed with cancer want to explore less conventional approaches first. They then have a fight on their hands to get the time they need to give those approaches a fair go. Not so for me. I wanted chemotherapy, radiotherapy the lot! Whatever they had on offer I wanted it. My consultant had to use all her considerable powers of persuasion to convince me that no, I was **not** going to die during those five weeks without treatment, and **yes**, it was safe to wait.

However, when I asked whether the treatment would cure my cancer, I was not reassured by her evasiveness. It seemed the best I could hope for was to have the disease 'contained' and that I should also expect to have ongoing chemotherapy.

Now, there is a rebellious and rather stubborn streak in me and, somehow, it took over while I waited for my results. The more information I found about the negative impact of chemotherapy on the body, the more I thought about my prognosis. I felt that 'containment of my disease' was just not good enough, damn it! I wanted to be free of it, completely. **Forever**.

This is what motivated me to start looking for and using alternative approaches to heal my body. My search brought me not only knowledge but also some very special people who played a vital part in my recovery. I include Dr. Patricia Clarke and Dr. Iain McGlinchey among these people.

I should actually give credit to Dr. McGlinchey for the title of this book. Now, before some of you get all excited and tell me that rabbits do get lymphoma, let me say this: I know that when we keep our pet rabbits all day in little hutches, with no access to daylight, when we vaccinate them and feed them an unnatural diet, rabbits too can get a multitude of diseases including lymphoma. No, my rabbits are of the wild and free variety. In any case, these words were meant as a joke and are an almost direct quote from Dr. McGlinchey. Indeed, many of my hospital appointments were made more tolerable by his cheery disposition and Dr. Clarke's bonhomie. Because they both dared to laugh with me, I felt that my humanity was being recognised and respected. I was still a human being first and foremost, even though I had cancer.

What follows is an account of my own leap into the unknown.

INTRODUCTION

I did not let the mere trifle of my complete lack of medical knowledge, or the fact that there was absolutely no guarantee of a successful outcome scare me into inaction, no. I took my life firmly into my own inexperienced hands and then, as a completely unforeseen consequence, I embraced that life with hitherto unknown passion.

I did not do this alone. Many people helped me, supported and guided me, sometimes unknowingly in so many different and wonderful ways. Some did so through the books they had written. I found comfort in their writings. Their beliefs and experiences gave me hope and spurred me on to make vital changes to my diet, to the way I saw myself and to the way I lived.

This book is my way of giving back a little of that which I received.

I hope it finds you, if you need it.

"RABBITS DON'T GET LYMPHOMA!"

Part One

MY STORY

Chapter One

SOMETHING'S UP!

'DO YOU THINK SHE'S PREGNANT?'

I tried not to smile. During my 15 years as a modern languages teacher, I had become adept at lip-reading. I had used this skill to great effect on my poor unsuspecting pupils who turned various shades of red when I was able to repeat word for word what they had taken great pains to keep from me. These two 11-year-old boys had been looking at my belly and were not concentrating on what I was trying to teach them. Shocking!

Actually, they had a point. I had noticed that my middle was getting rather big. I did indeed look pregnant. At nearly 45, with a history of unexplained infertility, I knew that was unfortunately out of the question. I must just have put on weight without noticing.

At home, I asked Ian, my long-suffering husband, for his opinion.

'What do you think? Do I look fat? Is my belly FAT?'

I stood in front of him holding and prodding the belly in question. I saw him cringe. When it came to the minefield of questions about my weight, Ian knew that no matter what he said, he couldn't win.

We had moved to Scotland three years previously when Ian was offered a post as a lecturer in Glasgow. It was a sudden and difficult move. Ian, having discovered a real talent for teaching, had applied for various posts all over the country. In July, he was offered a job at the Glasgow School of Art. He was due to start in September but I had not anticipated such a rapid chain of events. I was teaching full-time myself and had missed the three month deadline for handing in my notice.

So, Ian left for Scotland in late August and I remained in England until Christmas. We had never spent so long apart. Add to this the nightmare of selling the house on my own, in the middle of a recession, and you have a surefire recipe for some kind of health crisis. But I was a coper *par excellence, moi.* It would take a lot more than that to bring me down!

More trouble came in the shape of the landlord from hell who had rented us his deceased mother's house. It needed a lot of work done to make it habitable, but the landlord had promised faithfully that everything would be ready by the time we moved to Glasgow. However, when we arrived, after driving what felt like 8000 miles with as much furniture as we could cram into our car and our cat howling all the way from Essex to be told that the house wasn't ready, we were close to collapse. When it was suggested that perhaps we 'should go and stay in a wee hotel for a few days', we resisted the impulse to commit murder, we just took the keys and resigned ourselves to our fate. The rest of our furniture was being delivered the next day so we had no choice but to stay in the house overnight regardless of its state. There was a pile of rubble in the front room with an old gas heater on top. The house was like a building site, but we got our sleeping bags out, made a cup of tea in the filthy kitchen and spent the worst night ever on bare floorboards in one of the upstairs rooms. Our cat meowed angrily at us the whole night. She must have thought we had gone mad.

We only stayed three weeks in that hellhole and decamped early one morning after making a snowman in the front garden. A snowman, you ask? Yes, we thought we had to leave our landlord a token of our appreciation - it had two fingers sticking up in a 'V' sign!

More stress was still to come. We found a nice basement flat in a small town west of Glasgow. Ian commuted to work daily and I was to look for a suitable place to buy - oh and get a job too, of course. Eventually I did manage to find the perfect place for us. It took the best part of a year and a lot of persistence. Most of the estate agents were beginning to give me funny looks, some of them even told me to my face that they thought I was being far too fussy. Still, the hard work paid off, though I admit I did come very close to giving up hope of ever finding anything that felt right for us.

Finding a job also proved to be more arduous than I had anticipated. There simply seemed to be no teaching jobs around. Eventually, after nearly a whole year unemployed, I saw a post advertised in the local newspaper. It was in an independent school and it was only part-time, but beggars can't be choosers.

When I accepted the post, I knew deep down that I was making a big mistake. Yet, I did not listen to my feelings. Instead, I told myself that I should be grateful that I had found a job in a nice school with a good reputation. I reminded myself that working part-time was something I had longed for and now that I had the opportunity to do so, I would surely enjoy it.

Our mortgage repayments were another reason to start earning as soon as possible. They were twice the amount they had been when we lived in our little terraced house in England. Arrrgh! So, never mind that I felt like a fish out of the water in my new school, I told myself not to be silly, to stop whingeing and just get on with it. I was very good at bullying myself in those days.

So, I did my best but during the three years that I taught there, I never felt I belonged or that what I was doing had anything to do with education. In my previous post in a sixth form college in Colchester, the fact I was French had been an asset. Not so in this new school. I was convinced that absolutely anyone with only a smattering of French could have done as well if not better. We were all supposed to teach from files that had all the lessons outlined in detail. I should have loved it. One of my concerns in Colchester was that we had to constantly renew our teaching material to keep it up-to-date and interesting. It was indeed exciting to fly by the seat of my pants all the time, but it meant that there wasn't much time for anything else.

I should have stopped. I should have realised that teaching was no longer something I could do. But I guess my fear of being a bad teacher was surpassed by my fear of not being able to make ends meet.

I can see now that my repressed emotions, combined with the stress of moving home and leaving behind all the friends I had made in England, must have played a part in me getting sick. In fact, when I look back on the year before I was diagnosed, I can see that, quite apart from the bulging belly, there were other signs that all was not well with my health.

I had not been feeling quite myself for a few months. I had caught just about every virus going in the school and I seemed to be slightly feverish and at a low ebb most of the time. Not that I had any full-blown colds or flu, no, I just felt tired and lacking in 'oomph'. Once, when I thought I had a bad cold coming on, I remember thinking how weird it felt - as though my head was filled with water. To top it all, I had to go to the dental hospital in Glasgow to have a tooth extracted and an abscess treated. I had never had an abscess in my life and felt it was a sign that I was run down. Even more worrying for vain little me, my face had become quite puffy and worse still I could see that my hair was thinning!

I tried to convince myself it was all a figment of my imagination, or possibly due to a diet that relied overmuch on comfort foods, gallons of diet Orangina and not enough vegetables, which were usually found rotting at the bottom of my fridge. On really bad days, I saw the loss of my crowning glory as evidence that the menopause had me in its clutches. 'Yep – it's all downhill from now.' On those days, looking on the bright side seemed to be a faint, distant memory.

Although I realise this is probably not the impression I have given so far, I am basically an optimist at heart and usually do not wallow too long in my own self-pity. I was born under the sign of Taurus - the bull. I may remain still for a while, ponder and ruminate until something goes 'ping' in my head then, once fired up, nothing can stop me. So, in typical Taurean mode, I decided to tackle the belly issue head on.

I knew that my diet was far from healthy so I set about making some changes to it. As luck would have it, way back in the eighties, my friend Jeanie had bought me the book *Raw Energy* by Leslie Kenton. I had had a very quick look at it and then had put it on the shelf to read properly later. My exact thoughts were actually, 'Crikey - this looks like hard work, can't be bothered with that'. Well, later was now. Spurred on by my bulging abdomen, I decided to dust it off (the book, not the belly) and actually follow the diet.

A few months earlier my friend Christine, *cordon bleu* cook *par excellence*, had tried to get me to support an organic vegetable delivery scheme. Although I completely agreed with her on the benefits of an organic diet, I had not yet been motivated enough to place an order. Well, I now had the perfect reason to do so. I also started doing weird things like sprouting seeds and eating mung beans. My food processor was dragged out of its hiding place at the bottom of the cupboard and took up permanent residence on the work surface. At long last, after much cutting and slicing and grating, it started to lose its pristine shine!

I felt uncomfortably full most of the time on this new diet. I was not unduly concerned as I assumed it would take some time for my digestive system to adjust. I was however disappointed when there was no real change in the size or look of my abdomen. I even resorted to wearing 'Big Knickers' to fit into my clothes. Then, quite suddenly, my back started to play up. I felt a constant ache to the left of my spine, more or less were my left kidney was. I had also noticed a kind of bulge on the left side of my tummy while doing stomach 'crunches' - another desperate attempt to reduce the size of the belly - sad I know but true. It was as though I had an inflated balloon inside me! I could actually feel this swelling if I lay on my back and prodded around to the left of my belly button. It was not painful in any way, but it was hard and alien. As neither the pain nor the hard balloon was going away, I decided to go and see my GP.

Somewhere deep inside, alarm bells were ringing and I knew that something was wrong. Very wrong.

Chapter Two

I TOLD YOU I WAS SICK!

AFTER TAPPING MY BACK while fully clothed, my doctor thought I had a kidney infection and decided to put me on a course of antibiotics. I dutifully took them but felt frustrated and blamed myself for not specifically asking him to feel for the lump. I also regretted telling him that I had my period at the time. He probably thought that the swelling I had mentioned was just due to water retention and put my worries down to fluctuating hormones...

At school, I remember apologising to my pupils for the slightly disconnected way I had been teaching all that week. I felt slightly feverish and antibiotics always made me feel drowsy and nauseous. At times I had even spoken 'back to front' putting the last half of a word before the first one.

'I think I am a bit sick', I told them on the Friday afternoon. It probably came out as 'a bit thick' as I was also now slurring my words.

I didn't know it at the time but this was to be my last day as a teacher. I never got to say goodbye properly to any of my pupils and I had no idea what lay ahead of me. Just as well!

The next day was a Saturday and in full-blown all or nothing Taurean mode, I decided to eat only raw food!

That night, I felt awful. It was as if the whole of my digestive tract was full to bursting point. The feeling of tightness extended to my groin. Anxiety set in and I could not sleep at all. I got up and did something I usually tried to avoid because it scared the hell out of me - I looked for answers in *The Reader's Digest Family Medical Adviser*. Whenever I opened that book in search of an explanation for various symptoms, I always came to the conclusion that my days were numbered and that I was suffering from some rare and incurable disease. How ironic then that, when I needed it the most this book had nothing to offer, no label that could be attached to my unease.

Early on Sunday morning, I rang the emergency service at my local hospital and explained my symptoms to the doctor in charge. I expected him to tell me that I had overdone the raw food and that my digestive system was just struggling with all that fibre. However, instead of the reassuring words I had anticipated, this doctor asked me whether I could come to the hospital right away.

Suddenly, I felt a heavy, paralysing blackness descend upon me. For a while, it robbed me of all my strength and my ability to think or speak for myself.

Ian drove me to the hospital where, mercifully, we did not have to wait long. The doctor gave me a thorough examination and found the swelling in my abdomen. He seemed concerned he could not make it move. He called in a colleague who also examined me. Then they both went out of the room and asked Ian to accompany them.

I thought it must be very bad news indeed if they wanted to see Ian separately. The dreaded word - CANCER - came into my mind and kept bouncing off the sides of my otherwise inert brain. I felt I was going to die.

When they returned, they found me on the examining table, rocking myself back and forth, crying, desperate.

Both doctors tried to reassure me but, worryingly, said they wanted to schedule me for an ultrasound test the following day. One of them, when asked what could be the matter with me said, rather awkwardly I thought, that it could be a multitude of conditions ending in 'ma'. I remember that he did not look me in the eyes when he spoke and I knew he was being deliberately vague.

I can't remember much about the rest of that day. I know that I asked Ian what he and the doctors had discussed, whether they said I had cancer.

'No,' he replied, 'but they wanted to know whether there was a history of cancer in your family.'

What I do remember about that day and the days that followed, was looking at the brand new bed we had just bought and thinking with a sense of foreboding that I would not sleep in it for very long.

I took an overnight bag with me to the hospital as I had been told I might be admitted. I was more upset at the thought of having to stay in hospital than at having the tests done. For me, hospitals were the 'antechamber of death'. Hardly surprising, really, as I had only ever set foot in one of those dreaded places when one of my relatives had been receiving cancer treatment.

My heart was in my mouth when I got there. To make things worse, I was told there was no record of my booking for an ultrasound examination that day due to a lack of communication between departments. I would have to come back tomorrow, they said. This news, delivered without any hint of apology, came after what had seemed like an eternity of waiting in a ward.

I was totally unable to say or do anything for myself. If Ian had not been with me, I would probably have gone home like a docile little girl. But Ian was in no mood to comply. He was magnificent in his outrage! He announced quite loudly and forcefully, that there was no way we were going until we had seen somebody in authority who could sort out this mess.

To cut a long story short, I did eventually see a consultant. After much prodding of my abdomen, he announced that I probably had a kidney malformation. This reminded me that my father had suffered awful problems with one of his kidneys when he was in his 50s. The consultant looked serene and totally satisfied with his diagnosis. He had a group of students with him and had wafted into the ward, God like, with his 'disciples' in tow. I really wanted to believe him, but something I saw in one of the students' eyes made me feel that, had he been asked for his opinion, his diagnosis would have been quite different.

I was also given the ultrasound scan. The radiologist showed me a 'cyst' she had found, next to my descending aorta. I asked whether it was serious but she said she was not qualified to answer such a question. I found the ultrasound an uncomfortable procedure, even painful at times, when she had to press a little harder to get a clearer picture. The radiologist was surprised also.

As I was leaving the department, I heard footsteps running behind me. It was the radiologist. She put her hand on my shoulder and said that she could see how worried I was and that she had managed to get me a CT scan for next Tuesday. She explained that this should give me a clearer understanding of my condition. I was very grateful to her, as I had anticipated a much longer wait.

It didn't even enter my mind that I had been given such a fast appointment because something was very wrong indeed!

We waited for a decision about my possible stay in hospital. Eventually, after an excruciatingly long wait during which I sat on the edge of a bed, totally paralyzed and only just able to breathe, the consultant I had seen earlier told us there was no reason to admit me. What a relief! Although I was still concerned, the fact that I did not have to stay in the hospital one minute longer made me feel instantly better.

On the way home, my eyes were still filled with the image of that strange little balloon in my abdomen, the 'cyst' that had looked so harmless on the bright screen. Somehow, the word 'cyst' reassured me. I knew about cysts. I had one removed from my right breast when I was 15 years old. I hoped it would explain everything I had been feeling. I ran a very soothing dialogue with myself, in my head. Of course I had low backache, a cyst that size would cause my left kidney to be squeezed out of its normal position. Of course I felt uncomfortable after that meal, a cyst that size would compress my intestines. I was still a little disconcerted as to what could have caused this cyst to appear and how it would be removed, but seeing the culprit on the screen had been inexplicably reassuring. Nothing sinister there.

My GP rang a couple of days later to tell me that he had the results of my ultrasound scan and he had arranged for me to see a colleague of his as he was not going to be available. I had never met this colleague but instead of reassuring me, as I thought she would, she told me that the hospital must have suspected something serious. She explained that the speed of my referral for a CT scan was most unusual. When I asked what she thought was wrong with me, she said she could not really be sure until after the CT scan. It could be the result of a weird condition caused by a cat scratch, but it was more probably a form of lymphoma.

In all my years living in the UK, I had not come across that word; it sounded quite innocent, delicate, it could almost have been the name of a flower. For a minute, I escaped into a realm of fancy. 'Would you like some lymphoma in your bouquet, madam?'

'What exactly is lymphoma,' I heard myself ask. My voice sounded far, far away, as though it was an echo from another plane. A nanosecond later, her reply and the information it contained not only brought me back to the real world, but also ensured that all my illusions were well and truly shattered.

'It is a form of cancer of the lymphatic system' she explained and quickly added that she could call the haematology department at the Vale Hospital. She would make an appointment for me to see a specialist who could tell me more about it.

I must have agreed because she made the phone call. As luck would have it, I could see a haematologist that very afternoon.

'Is it curable?' I managed to ask her through my totally parched lips.

'Some are treatable,' came the cautious reply.

I wanted to call Ian at work so he could accompany me to the hospital. She took me to another room and left after telling me that somebody would look in shortly. I made my call to a very distraught husband. He had wanted to go to the surgery with me that morning, but I had told him I felt fine. It was only a cyst after all.

A receptionist brought me a glass of water and left. Alone, I drank my water. It was cool but, although my mouth was dry, it had no impact on me. My whole body had turned to ice. My mind seemed frozen. Time stood completely still.

After what felt like an eternity, some form of life came back to me and I got up. I walked past the reception desk in what felt like slow motion. The receptionist glanced at me and looked away. I left. I walked home like a zombie and waited for Ian.

That afternoon, we saw a very kind haematologist who told us there were many different types of lymphoma, there were treatments that could help, it was not a type of cancer that usually spread to other systems and organs, metastasised, so it could be contained. He also mentioned the name of my consultant for the first time and assured me that Dr. Clarke would be his choice if he had lymphoma,

'She's great,' he enthused.

As he opened the door to his office and said goodbye, I felt compelled to ask, in a vain attempt to sound unperturbed by my possibly imminent departure from this world:

'So, I am not at death's door then?'

'Not by a long shot,' he answered warmly, looking straight into my eyes.

His reply, although succinct, contained enough hope to keep me from falling into an abyss of despair.

Chapter Three

WITH LUCK ON MY SIDE

A FEW DAYS LATER I met my consultant, Dr. Patricia Clarke. Ian was with me and did most of the talking. In those first few days, when I felt robbed of all my energy and strength, he was there fighting for me.

Dr. Clarke explained that, to give me the appropriate dose of chemotherapy and/or radiotherapy, they needed to know exactly what type of lymphoma I had, what grade it was. What? This thing has different grades? I thought. Yes, I could still just about think.

They wanted to do more tests to determine whether mine was a slow growing lymphoma developed over say, the last couple of years, or whether it had only been there a few months and was therefore a very aggressive type. I was also told that some slow-growing lymphomas have been known to mutate into more aggressive forms.

I tried to take in all this information, I really did, but to no avail. My brain seemed to be filled with a dense fog and nothing was getting through. However, even though my thought processes had ground to a halt, my feelings on the other hand were in overdrive. The message I got from deep within my gut was that this 'Thing' could never be expected to follow a set pattern and I could never relax and know where I was going. Not good, not good at all.

Dr. Clarke also told me it would take at least a fortnight to get the results of all the tests, since two separate teams had to perform them and then compare notes.

Suddenly, I realised that it would take some time before I could begin treatment for my condition. I had not expected that. This enforced delay was quite frustrating and I felt scared that lumps were going to start popping up all over my body.

In the meantime, a biopsy and bone marrow aspiration were immediately scheduled for that afternoon. Fortunately, Dr. Clarke had no other procedures to perform that day.

'Jolly good,' I said emulating the famous British Stiff Upper Lip, 'What a jolly piece of luck!'

We all laughed and the sound of my own laughter brought me some relief from the all-pervading numbness that had taken hold of me.

Looking back, I am amazed at how easily everything seemed to connect, how quickly and smoothly the tests seemed to interweave. It did not feel like that at the time. In fact, I am surprised how much of this I remember since I was in a state of shock for most of these tests. Then it felt surreal, as though it were happening to somebody else.

What I connected with immediately, though, was the warmth, friendliness, sense of humour and empathy shown by Dr. Clarke. She was very straightforward in the explanations she gave and, yes, she did look me in the eyes when she spoke.

She stressed the positive about my particular condition - the fact that it had probably been developing over quite some time, that no vital organs were in immediate danger, that my condition was controllable, if not curable and that I was quite fit.

She said many other things, mostly to Ian, but the message that was coming to me, loud and clear, was that I could trust her as a consultant and, more importantly perhaps, as a human being.

Her colleague, Dr. McGlinchey, performed a biopsy on my largest abdominal lump that afternoon. I remember, and I trust he can forgive me should he ever read these lines, hoping that his aim was better than his eyesight appeared to be. The machine he was going to use had the longest needle I had ever seen and I imagined I would be skewered like a piece of chicken on a kebab, if his aim were not totally accurate!

I was told to relax before the needle was fired into my abdomen.

'RELAX? You've got to be joking', I thought. Even the nurse had to look away. Surprisingly, and no doubt due to the niftily applied small dose of anaesthetic, I did not feel a thing and I did not end up nailed to the operating table.

Immediately afterwards, I was wheeled to another room where my consultant performed the bone marrow aspiration.

Aspiration? That had to be another joke! I renamed the procedure "Excavation", a far more accurate term for having one's spine drilled in order to get to the precious marrow. Thank God for anaesthetics! In fact, the type I was given made me quite talkative. I am not exactly sure how it happened, but Ian remembers me teaching Dr. Clarke and the nurse who was assisting some filthy French swearwords! He was amazed at the amount of laughter, my own included, that seemed to be coming from the cubicle where this delicate operation was taking place.

After dressing and waiting a while for my head to clear, I was introduced to a young man who was, according to his identity tag, a Macmillan nurse. His job was to let me know what to expect regarding the side effects of treatment. I told him that I hoped my type of lymphoma was not an aggressive one. To my astonishment, he disagreed. According to him, aggressive lymphomas responded better to chemotherapy whereas slow evolving ones were more difficult to treat. I know he was trying to help me, but his words made me realise suddenly that nothing about this 'damned thing' was as expected. Since when had an aggressive cancer been easier to treat than a slow one? However, this realisation was but a brief moment of lucidity in a day where mostly, I felt quite disconnected, no doubt due to the anaesthetic left in my body.

I looked at the various leaflets he had given me. They were mostly about hair loss and what to do about it. I only remember the various 'creative' ways you could wrap a scarf around a bald head to disguise it. I laughed hysterically at the pictures. This, I decided, did not and could not possibly apply to me. If I lost my hair, I would get the best wig I could afford and maybe try a different colour while I was at it. Did I see myself as a redhead? You bet I did!

Chapter Four

WHAT'S THE ALTERNATIVE?

DURING MY LAST YEAR AT SCHOOL, I sensed that change was going to happen whether I liked it or not. I could see that part-timers were expendable as it was thought we did not represent good value for money. I decided I had better find some other way of earning a living. But identifying that 'something else' was easier said than done, I didn't have a clue where to start. Teaching had been my one true vocation. How could I ever replace it with anything as meaningful to me?

I decided to let my heart lead me in the right direction. Thinking was no good and just made me fretful and confused. I went to the local library and took out all the files I could find on what people did for a living. There was one on alternative therapies. As I dabbled in aromatherapy at home, I looked more closely at the various therapies described within the file and something called reflexology caught my eye. I don't know why exactly, but working with people's feet was strangely appealing. So, I let my intuition guide me for once and soon started a course in Glasgow. I was just about to sit my final exam when I was diagnosed.

I made a couple of good friends on that course and one of them, Meg, when she heard about my cancer suggested I contact someone she knew - Graham was his name. She had been receiving treatment from this man for a while and felt he would be able to help me. He had practised reflexology for over ten years and was a 'fountain of knowledge and expertise' on anything 'alternative'.

This is how I came to meet Graham.

There is a saying, the origin of which I forget, and it goes something like this, 'When the student is ready, the master appears'. I know Graham would object very strongly to my describing him as a 'master' for he is far too modest a man. I do feel, however, that I was on a quest for knowledge and that it was no mere coincidence that he came into my life at that precise moment. Synchronicity, some call it.

Although very unassuming in his demeanour, Graham was definitely not shy when it came to putting his point of view across. His opinion regarding chemotherapy fell on me much like the blade of the guillotine would have. It shattered my as yet unquestioned and somewhat blind faith in this treatment. For Graham, chemotherapy was a barbaric approach that totally destroyed your immune system and, quite simply, killed you in the process.

I am sure he must have seen the look of total and utter shock on my face as he quickly suggested that I should go and see someone he knew, a naturopath, in Glasgow. This expert had successfully treated many conditions like mine and would no doubt be able to advise me regarding the best course of action. After recovering from my stupor I went home and made an appointment to see his colleague. I thought it would not hurt to get another opinion.

Poor Graham - his plan backfired. After examining me, the naturopath was so aghast at the size of my abdominal lymph nodes that he actually advised me to have chemo-therapy! He had apparently never come across such large tumours before and was eager for one of his colleagues to examine me too. I declined. I had been poked and prodded enough, thank you very much.

Disappointed, he announced he was sorry that he could not be of assistance. He also stated, quite categorically, that alternative methods only worked if you believed in them. He must have written me off as a 'non-believer'.

However, my appointment was not a complete waste of time. This wise man did give me a really useful piece of advice. He told me to go for walks in nature and really com-mune with the elements, to hug trees. (Pardon?) He explained that there is a lot of healing energy in trees and that it would help me get stronger. I left his practice feeling puzzled to say the least and completely at a loss as to what to do next.

Later on though, the idea of communing more deeply with nature made a lot of sense. That is, after I had recovered from the mind-boggling vision of myself hugging trees.

I had always been an outdoor kind of person, a bit of a tomboy in my teens. I was often found up a tree with my friend Pierric. Later, when I lived in England, Ian and I joined a cycling club. We would go for long tandem rides most weekends and I felt really elated flying down small country lanes.

A wonderful memory had also resurfaced of me galloping through the forest many moons ago, when I was a troubled teenager. After the usual Saturday morning's altercation with my mother, I had arrived late to the riding school. The group had already left for its long-awaited first outing in the woods. So, I was given a horse. I was told to put a saddle on it and to get 'cracking' if I wanted to catch up with them. Someone fetched the master's dog, an Alsatian, to show me the way. His eager face told me that he knew exactly what was expected of him. I had no time to protest, doubt or fret. I just got on and off we went.

A miracle happened that day, for once I had no difficulty staying in the saddle! I forgot to worry about my lack of ability and had but one thought in my mind, catching up with the rest of the group. Because I took no notice of my body, I must have relaxed so completely I even found that mysterious "seat" my teacher had lectured me about and that had eluded me until then. I felt at one with the galloping horse and my wolf-like companion; we seemed united by the same intention.

How can I convey the sense of utter freedom I experienced in those blissful moments? The muffled sound of hooves on fallen leaves, the warm musty scent of the forest on that beautiful autumn afternoon, the magnificent stag we encountered at close range, his deep dark eyes, all this is forever etched in my heart. I felt connected to who I was and the whole of Creation as never before. This was one of the defining moments of my life and its echo came back to me when I needed courage and trust in my own strength. Suddenly, I knew exactly what the naturopath meant by 'communing with nature'. I felt the memory of that day course through my veins. Well, I thought, I certainly have picked the right country for my purpose. There is an abundance of wild, open, achingly magnificent countryside in Scotland and some of the best was right on my doorstep.

I went back to Graham and reported on the naturopath's verdict. The poor man was struck totally and absolutely speechless for a few moments. (That was a first, let me tell you.) The look of complete disbelief on his face was actually quite comical. He was livid but managed to utter through gritted teeth, that he had 'a good mind to phone him and demand an explanation'. Mercifully, he calmed down and decided instead to work with me three times a week using reflexology and Reiki.

Graham revealed many years later that he had hoped this knowledgeable naturopath would take me on as a patient. He felt the burden of responsibility for my health was too great for him alone to carry. I was shocked when I realised I had caused him such stress. I was also immensely grateful that he had somehow found the courage to carry this 'burden'. But he was wrong.

The responsibility for my health was mine and mine alone.

I was amazed at how different I felt after each session. I would arrive anxious and only too aware of weird aches and pains in my abdominal area. I would leave serene, full of hope and with a spring in my step. Somehow my time with him put all my pieces back together and I was whole again.

My reflexology training had already begun to open my mind about the body's amazing potential for healing itself. Listening to Graham made me realise that it might well recover from just about anything, even cancer, given the right encouragement and support. For the first time I began to wonder whether there might be another possible way of dealing with my disease. I knew that I was not satisfied with just 'controlling' my cancer, I wanted it out of me completely, irrevocably.

I owe Graham so much. He opened my eyes to another world. He showed me that I could follow another path where body, mind, emotions and spirit were all connected.

It was a tough awakening, as it dawned on me that I had probably played a part in getting this disease. I knew that I had kept so much of my true self under lock and key for most of my adult life. I had ignored the stirrings of my soul for so long that it was now speaking to me, in no uncertain terms, through my disease. I had been enslaved by many fears for far too long and so my spirit gave me the greatest fear of all, my own death, to face up to. Kind of logical when you think about it.

Well, I told myself, it's time to find my courage, be myself at long last and try and find a way to repair this mess. As it happens, Graham lent me a book, a small yellow book with a picture of Rudolph Breuss, an elderly gentleman wearing glasses, on the front cover. It had an impossibly long title *Advice for the prevention and natural treatment of numerous diseases, Cancer, Leukaemia and other seemingly incurable diseases.* Yet, rather than finding such a book off-putting, I felt really drawn to it and to this little photograph of him. The eyes glowed with intelligence and kindness. I also saw a hint of rebelliousness in them, which greatly appealed to me. I don't know whether you have noticed but I read a lot in people's eyes. Okay, so you had noticed.

My heart beat a little faster as I held the book and allowed its energy to communicate itself to me. I started reading it that day. Although I found nothing in his book regarding lymphoma, I felt that his approach to leukaemia could be helpful. Basically you ate a normal diet, preferably organic, but cut out red meat and pork. You also drank special herbal teas during the day to detoxify and support the body. A special vegetable juice also featured and varying amounts had to be drunk daily.

I liked Rudolph Breuss's approach and the way he wrote about it, his passion was contagious. At some very deep level, his method 'spoke' to me and made perfect sense.

The book also mentioned that for this treatment to work, it should be tried **before** any form of chemotherapy. That was something I was going to have to talk to Dr. Clarke about. I wondered how she would take the news.

A week or so before meeting Graham, I had gone to the hospital to have the results of my CT scan explained to me. They confirmed the original diagnosis. My lymphoma was a non-Hodgkin's type, with features 'typical of a follicle centre cell lymphoma' and 'would be regarded as Low Grade in the Kiel classification and grade one in the REAL classification'. This is a direct quote from my medical notes at the time. I still don't know exactly, nor do I care what some of those terms mean, but Dr. Clarke explained they meant that my cancer was not an aggressive type. Consequently, she felt there was no rush to start treatment right away. None of my vital organs seemed at risk from the enlarged nodes. However, their size was of concern to her and she thought there might still be a chance that my cancer could mutate into a more aggressive form. Because this would impact on the type of chemotherapy I could receive, she elected to wait a few more weeks and observe it.

I found this 'doing nothing' approach utterly bewildering. How could it be right when they knew I had **cancer** for goodness sake!

At home, my fertile imagination was working overtime. I

would anxiously prod every inch of my body to check the size of my lymph nodes and convince myself I had discovered yet another 'lump'. My heart would suddenly beat furiously, my brain turned into a porridge-like substance and my breathing virtually stopped. The feeling of dread was so intense it was suffocating. My mind would fall into the clutches of hysteria. Panic oozed out of every pore of my body. This was the state I was in when I first met Graham - the poor man.

But what a difference a few days make. I armed myself with Rudolf Breuss's book and took it with me to my next hospital appointment. I asked my bewildered consultant what she thought of his approach, making it very clear that I had every intention of following his 'advice'. I handed her the book and asked for her opinion. Despite her surprise, she did look at it. She admitted she knew nothing of this way of dealing with cancer. She certainly had never heard of people getting better through diet alone. On the other hand, she understood that it would give me some form of control while I waited. I suppose she had already worked out what kind of a patient I was and realised that I probably would go out of my tiny mind if I did not start **doing** something soon.

Although she had her reservations, Dr. Clarke agreed that she could not really see how this approach would harm me. She was concerned, however, that I might lose too much weight on the diet (chance would be a fine thing!) and that chemotherapy might be compromised when the time came.

So, she decided to monitor my progress very closely to make sure this did not happen.

I realise now how amazingly lucky I was. Not for me the agonising decision about which route to follow first. Not for me either the browbeating that most conventionally trained consultants and doctors feel obliged to give their patients, if they dare mention 'alternatives', that dirty word.

I probably needed this amount of luck at the beginning. A more arrogant consultant may have tried to crush my spirit and ridiculed my efforts. Who can say where that would have led? Maybe to the front page of *The Sun* newspaper, 'Crazed Cancer Patient Cracks - Strangles Consultant with Bare Hands'.

I was also reassured by the fact that Dr. Clarke was not going to abandon me. I would see her every fortnight or so and she would check my blood and the way my lymph nodes were behaving.

Ian and I went home that day and I phoned a reputable herbalist in England who kept the precise herbs recommended by 'dear old Rudolph Breuss'. He told me that the Biotta Company produced the organic vegetable cocktail which Breuss recommended and where I could get it in Scotland. He also informed me that a woman with non-Hodgkin's lymphoma had gone on the recommended 28 day juice fast, but it hadn't worked for her. My heart sank at this news but I wondered whether she might not have been more successful on the approach I was going to take, following a more normal diet of organic produce but without meat, except a little chicken, plus the juice and special teas too. The teas arrived the next day and I started my new regime very soon after that.

I also raided Graham's extensive collection of books on cancer treatment and bought quite a few of my own. From that day on, I read and read and read some more. The more I read, the more I realised that it was not just my body that needed to heal - my emotions were out of control, my self image was a mass of negativity and, as for my spirit, it was almost broken. A diet alone was not going to give me all the answers I needed, but I had to start somewhere. So, I did.

Chapter Five

RESULTS!

I BOUGHT SEVERAL BOTTLES of Biotta Breuss juice, I made his kidney tea and his sage tea and drank them according to his instructions. I also used the cranesbill tea he mentioned in his book as it is meant to help your body eliminate the by-products of radiation. I had read that lymphomas are possibly linked to radiation damage. Did I mention that I happened to be out cycling when the Chernobyl nuclear cloud burst over England? Or that we had moved to an area near a nuclear submarine base? As a consequence, I felt that this tea would help.

I also started my 'return to Nature' program immediately and eagerly looked for a walk that would be interesting enough to do each day and not overlong.

There is a beautiful hill where I 'stay', as some people say in Scotland. The path leads upwards through lovely wooded areas and up to its heather covered top. From the cairn, you can see the island of Arran on a clear day and the Arrochar Alps to the north. It is a lovely walk which takes a couple of hours, door to door so to speak. I decided to make it part of my daily exercise regime.

This walk delivered an unforeseen blessing to me.

The first time I walked through the wood at the foot of the hill, I came upon a tree that was to become a real symbol of recovery for me, a message about life going on in spite of everything.

It was a huge beech tree. It had obviously been struck down by a storm at some point. Its trunk rested on the ground and its roots were exposed in all their intricate, delicate swirls. And yet, the tree was still alive! Its foliage was as plentiful and luxuriant if not more so, than the other beeches around. There seemed to be only one root still diving into the ground but that one, strong root was enough to sustain such a magnificent tree. It was all it needed to continue to get nourishment from the earth below, all it needed to go on living. I stood there, mesmerised. After a while, I felt drawn to the tree and compelled to place my arms around its trunk. I could not believe that I was doing it but, yes, I was hugging a tree! I was identifying myself with a tree. A wonderful feeling of peace filled me as my hands touched the moss-covered bark. That feeling is still with me now, 10 years later.

Whenever I walk to the top of the hill, I always make a point of stopping to have a chat with 'my' tree, to feel 'his' strength, to thank 'him' for sharing it with me. As ridiculous as this may seem to some of you, this was my way of re-connecting with the power of Nature and quite possibly, with life itself.

To start with, I had weekly check-ups at the hospital. Dr. Clarke wanted to make sure that my lymph nodes were not getting any larger. The technique used to do so made me laugh each time. She would take a tape measure out of her pocket and feel the largest lump in my abdomen. The said lump would then be measured from one end to the other.

'Very high tech.' Ian and I would say.

'Certainly,' she would reply, 'no expense spared here.'

Each time, she would confirm that the lump was no bigger. Soon, she even said that it felt a little smaller. I remember looking at Ian and punching the air in triumph. Dr. Clarke smiled. However, she also pointed out that this was in no way inconsistent with this disease; lumps tended to get smaller and then would enlarge again. The reduction would have to persist for her to get excited, she said. I, on the other hand, felt sure that my diet and my new approach on life were having the desired effect.

I continued to read and found more information on juicing as a therapy to fight cancer. I read about Max Gerson, his institute in New Mexico and his regime, carried on by his daughter Charlotte after his death. The Gerson approach to treating cancer consists in having patients drink a vegetable cocktail several times a day; in using coffee enemas to help the liver release stored toxicity and other enemas to cleanse the bowels. His approach also requires you to take liver extract and some supplements. I found it all absolutely fascinating and I still do not know why I did not give it a try. It just didn't 'speak' to me in the same way the Breuss diet did, but it nonetheless made me think.

I felt somehow that, if I could drink fresh juices instead of the bottled ones, I would allow my body to benefit from a lot more goodness.

At that point, in another amazing 'coincidence' Jan, a lovely colleague of mine from school, lent me a book about juicing. It contained recipes for cancer-fighting juices and a diet designed to boost the body's main defence mechanism, the immune system. The diet was very similar to the one recommended by Rudolph Breuss, but the juices contained ingredients that were far more readily available in this country. I decided to give this a go and purchased a juicer forthwith.

The company delivering my organic vegetables, fruit and other essentials must have thought they had 'died and gone to heaven' when I placed my first amended order - 15kgs of carrots for a start! Yes, as you can imagine, the amount of money we were allocating to our food budget soared from one day to the next. However, when faced with the prospect of your own death in the not too distant future, it is a lot easier to focus your mind on what really matters.

Yes, we really could have done with changing our car for a newer one, ours was the object of many derogatory comments from friends - 'diseased' some called it. Others went further and remarked that its rust-encrusted bonnet 'looked like the plague' and wondered whether it was catching? We laughed along with our cheeky friends. Material possessions meant nothing all of a sudden. Living life to the full was all that mattered. It still is.

I started my new diet and adapted what I had read to my own needs and according to the way my body responded. After a couple of months of regular juicing, increasing my intake of raw vegetables, whole grains, and cutting out my 'comfort foods' (you know the ones I mean - biscuits, chocolate, cakes, sweets) I began to notice changes in my physical appearance. On the plus side, I was losing weight fast. However, my chin was quite literally covered in very strange spots. 'Little white pyramids' is the best way I could describe them and I turned a shockingly bright shade of orange. I did not worry however as I had read that this was a normal reaction to the body getting rid of a lot of toxins and my new 'skin tone' was due to a harmless accumulation of beta-carotene.

I felt incredibly energised and optimistic. As toxicity accumulated over years of self-neglect left my cells, my mind became clearer, calmer; I felt joyful, grateful and at peace most of the time. I felt as though I was connecting with people, with the world around me, with life itself, in a much more profound way. Everything around me became more precious. The sky, the trees and the hills, the Clyde even, seemed to resonate with an intensity that I had not experienced before. I had reconnected with my soul and all my relationships were affected by this transformation.

The diet was helping my body fight back, but it was not the only change I made.

I set about trying to harness the power of my mind and my spirit by meditating twice a day and by doing visualisation exercises. Among the many books that I read avidly, *Getting Well Again* by Carl O. Simonton, Stephanie Matthews-Simonton and James Creighton intrigued me. It extolled the merits of visualisation. This technique is proven to have greatly helped people with cancer. It apparently enhances the efficiency of chemotherapy and reduces the damage to healthy cells. It can also be used instead of drugs, in a 'mind over matter' approach to disease.

Fired with irrepressible enthusiasm, I drew on A4 paper something that looked like a pathetic effort to enter a cartoon competition. My white 'killer' cells, in the guise of little piranha fish with great pointed teeth and very focused, friendly eyes, were seeking out and devouring my shrivelled and grey-looking cancerous cells. I liked that picture so much that I even added sound to it.

'Miam miam miam,' went the piranhas as they gobbled up my diseased cells, 'yum yum yum!'

After a while I didn't even have to make an effort to visual-ise them. It was as though I had a permanently switched on television in my head showing this cartoon, over and over. Wherever I went, whoever I was with or speaking to, the TV screen was lit up and the sound was on.

I also needed help with my emotions. I had read Lawrence LeShan's beautiful book *Cancer As A Turning Point* and had come to realise the terrifying power of repressed emotions. My friend Stephanie, also a reflexologist, had lent me Louise Hay's book, *You Can Heal Your Life* soon after I was diagnosed. I had read a few pages and thought with typical Gallic scorn 'This woman is nuts' and promptly tossed the book aside.

Well, never say, never! A few months down the line I found that my mind had opened up sufficiently for me to revisit her concepts about healing past hurts using affirmations. I looked at the middle section of her book where lots of diseases were listed in alphabetical order. Next to each disease was a set of probable emotional causes. As usual, I found no mention of 'non-Hodgkin's lymphoma' anywhere.

Undeterred, I looked up 'Hodgkin's disease', not expecting much. Well, you could have 'knocked me down with a feather' as the saying goes. Her words could have been written just for me.

'Blame and tremendous fear of not being good enough. A frantic race to prove one's self until the blood has no substance left to support itself. The joy of life is forgotten in the race for acceptance.'[2]

So there it was, my life laid bare in those few words.

The last sentence still echoing in my mind, I glanced at the affirmation designed to erase the negativity of such thoughts and fears. It was disappointingly, quite a lengthy one.

'I am perfectly happy to be me,' (yeah, right!) 'I am good enough just as I am,' (who, me?) 'I love and approve of myself,' (you're kidding, right?) 'I am joy expressing and receiving' (Pardon?)

I was supposed to say this over and over. At first, I was to use a mirror and look deep into my eyes as I was saying the affirmation.

Well, this proved a lot tougher than you might think. I just could not do it. My attempts at looking in the mirror failed miserably, either through irrepressible fits of the giggles, or through floods of tears. As a last resort, I chose to just keep to, 'I love and approve of myself. All is well.' That was challenging enough. After a while, I had a breakthrough. I found I could use the mirror and mean what I was saying, at least a little.

I decided to use this same principle to further encourage my immune system to heal. I looked into mirrors, windows and oven doors, anything that would reflect my face back at me and say, as though I was having a conversation with someone, 'My immune system is very strong, you know' It was fun, made me laugh and by this time I believed every word of it.

The nights were my toughest challenge. I would wake up suddenly literally shaking with fear. However, from the moment I started using those affirmations and the piranha visualisation, I was able to go back to sleep quite quickly. Later, no sooner would I register being awake than I would hear my affirmations and the delighted 'yum yums' of my killer cells in my head, as if I had a tape on constant replay implanted in the middle of my brain. Later still, I realised that I was no longer waking up at all and that the fear was no more.

I had my first CT scan on 6 May 1998. It reported '...extensive intra-abdominal adenopathy from the level of the renal hilum downwards...' Tumours in my belly. Lots of them. Both my kidneys were apparently surrounded by similar 'adenopathy' together with 'several small cysts' on my liver.

On 1 July 1998, an ultra-sound scan of my abdomen concluded that my largest tumours appeared 'somewhat smaller'. No mention of any cysts on my liver. The final sentence made me smile when I saw it a couple of years later, as I was gathering material for this book. It read, 'There appears to have been some improvement despite the lack of conventional treatment.'

These results suitably impressed Dr. Clarke. She saw no reason to start chemotherapy since 'whatever' I was doing seemed to be working so far. I could see she was at a loss to explain why indeed 'this' was working. In her experience, nothing like this had happened before and I guess she was concerned about making the wrong decision in not starting chemotherapy. I owe a lot to her courage. However I could have easily put her mind at rest, had she voiced those doubts to me, as there was **zero** chance of me going along with chemotherapy now.

I continued with my regime and thrice weekly reflexology and Reiki sessions. When I had doubts, when I became frustrated because 'this thing' was not yet obliterated, I would mention it to Graham as he worked on my feet. He helped me see I had nothing to fear, whatever the outcome. He gave me some more books to read. I looked forward to my talks with him and to the very deep peace that would envelop me as a result of the treatment and of his reassuring presence.

Soon, during one of Dr. Clarke's high-tech 'proddings' around my abdomen, a real change could be felt. My most accessible lump was definitely smaller and more importantly, its consistency was much softer.

'Is that good?' I remember asking. 'Yes, very good.' came her firm reply.

I had another CT scan on 16 September 1998. This is what the report of that scan said:

'Despite the rather unconventional therapy... (the) mass continues to get better.'

This was followed by a lot of technical details. I remember that Dr. Clarke read out the conclusion which had been written by her colleague, Dr. McGlinchey. She seemed to be struggling to contain her hilarity.

'It says here that there is a reduction of 75 percent of your mass. My colleague concludes with this message, "Eat more vegetables," she chuckled. With great excitement, Dr. Clarke showed me the films of my scan over a lit background so that I could see a before and after of my 'adenopathy'.

'If we had achieved these results with chemotherapy, we would be really chuffed,' she added candidly. God bless her!

The feeling of elation stayed with me that whole day. It remained, despite getting a speeding ticket on my way back from the hospital. I realise now that I should not really have driven anywhere that day. I was drunk with happiness.

I had another ultrasound scan on 16 December 1998. It noted only 'a single 3 x 2 x 2.3cm lymph node' remaining near my right kidney and pancreas.

What a blow that was. I had forgotten about that side of my abdomen in my visualisations believing, wrongly, that the mass lay mostly to the left. I decided there and then to really concentrate on that final rogue node and zap it back into shape.

Almost a year to the day after the initial diagnosis of my condition, I had another CT scan. Dr. McGlinchey, who performed most of those tests and used to welcome me with a cheery, 'Ah, it's Bugs Bunny' entered my medical history thus:

'Lymphoma (treated by carrots)!

'CT CHEST, ABDOMEN & PELVIS

'The previously noted adenopathy is now extremely difficult to define.'

The report ended with these words:

'The features are further improved and represent greater
than 90 percent remission from the original scans.'

A couple of months later, after an ultrasound scan, (no
more radiation from CT scans for me, thank you very much!)
I was finally given the news I was so longing to hear. Reading
through the report again for the purpose of writing this
book, I was amazed not to say disappointed, that such a
momentous event deserved no more than 'Normal liver etc.'
and 'no adenopathy'.

Well I never! So, it was true after all.

All that I had read in all these books explaining how
wonderful and powerful our bodies were; how they knew
how to return to a state of balance, given the right conditions, all this was really true?

No adenopathy?

No, actually, bloody brilliant!

✳   ✳   ✳

A FEW SCARY PICTURES

Ultrasound Scan

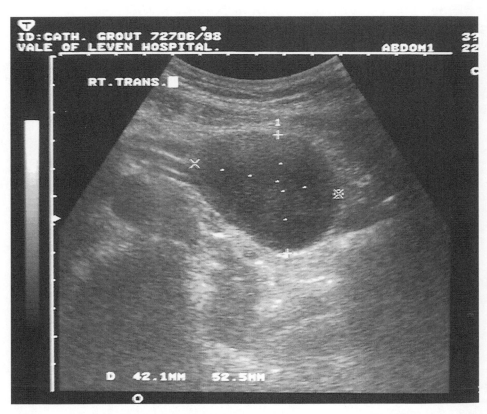

Figure 1. View of right transverse (colon area probably) 1998.
First ultrasound scan. .

Ultrasound Scan

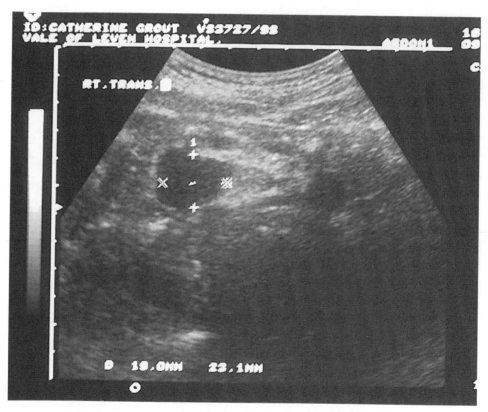

Figure 2. 16th December 1998.
Several months after initial diagnosis. Ultrasound scan.

CT Scan

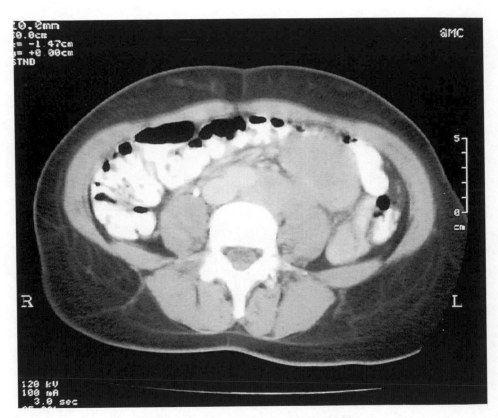

Figure 3. CT scan done in May 1998.
The tumours show up as black holes.
Looks as if my abdomen is like gruyère cheese, doesn't it?

CT Scan

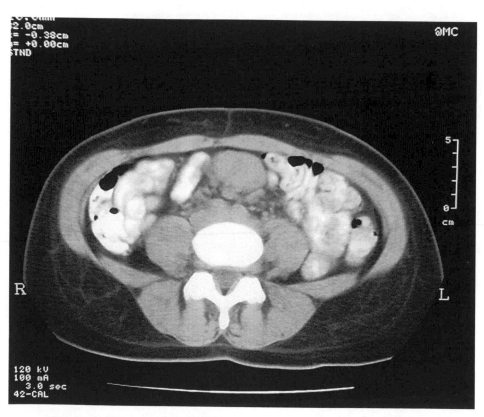

Figure 4. CT scan 15/9/1998. Four months after the initial CT scan.

Extracts from Consultant's Notes

```
              VALE OF LEVEN X-RAY REPORT
Patient : CATHERINE GROUT   Status : IP          Reg: 232401
Referred: MR J.R. MACCALLUM WARD 1 SURGICAL      DOB: 24 Apr 1953
         SURGICAL UNIT VOLDGH, MAIN ST.          PGE: 1

Other requests also reported.            Referred by         Exam date
V68283    ABDOMEN KUB                    J.R. MACCALLUM   WD:001 26/04/98

U/S OF UPPER ABDOMEN
Extensive para-aortic lymph adenopathy was outlined and was seen to
extend into pelvis.  Small 13 mm sono-lucent lesion was outlined in
right lobe of liver.  Otherwise no abnormality was seen in liver,
spleen region of pancreas, gall bladder or either kidney.  No free
fluid was present.  No abnormality was seen in pelvic organs.

IMPRESSION
Extensive para-aortic and pelvic lymphadenopathy.  CT scan of thorax
and abdomen has been arranged for this patient next week.  Probable
benign small cystic lesion in right lobe of liver.

ABDOMEN
Residue is present throughout large bowel without evidence to suggest
obstruction.  No pathological calcification or significant
abnormality is seen.


Typed : 27 Apr 1998 (L.B) Reported : Dr. P.W.  GILL
```

```
Patient : CATHERINE GROUT   Status : OP          Reg: 232401
Referred: DR H.A. CARMICHAEL                     DOB: 24 Apr 1953
         MEDICAL UNIT VOLDGH, MAIN ST.           PGE: 1

HISTORY
Abdominal mass.

CT CHEST, ABDOMEN & PELVIS
The chest, abdomen and pelvis have been examined in 10/15mm slices
with I.V. contrast enhancement.
There is no evidence of disease within the axillae, mediastinum or
lung fields.  There is extensive intra-abdominal adenopathy from the
level of the renal hilum downwards.  There is an area of confluent
adenopathy lying anterior to the inferior pole of the right kidney and
extending across the mid line anterior to the IVC.  There is a further
rounded area of adenopathy inferior to the left kidney which is in
direct contact with the anterior abdominal wall.  This measures
4.6 x 5.6 cms at slice 2.25 and would be amenable to percutaneous
ultrasound guided biopsy if required.  The adenopathy extends into the
pelvis asymmetrically into the right side.  The right iliac adenopathy
measures 2.4 x 3.4 cms at slice 2.31.  Unfortunately this does not
extend below the inguinal ligament.  Several small cysts are noted in
the liver.  Kidneys and spleen are normal.

CONCLUSION


Typed : 06 May 1998 (L.B) Reported : Dr. IAIN  McGLINCHEY
```

56

```
                    VALE OF LEVEN X-RAY REPORT
Patient : CATHERINE GROUT   Status : 0          Reg: 232401
Referred: MR A UNKNOWN SURG CON                 DOB: 24 Apr 1953
          X,X                                   PGE: 1
```

HISTORY
Lymphoma.

U/S BIOPSY
Under direct ultrasound guidance three 15 gauge cores were taken from
the most superficial lesion to the left of the mid line. Uneventful
procedure.

```
                    VALE OF LEVEN X-RAY REPORT
Patient : CATHERINE GROUT   Status : 0          Reg: 232401
Referred: DR P. CLARKE                          DOB: 24 Apr 1953
          HAEMATOLOGY UNIT VOLDGH,MAIN ST.      PGE: 1
```

HISTORY
Lymphoma.

U/S OF ABDOMEN
The large lesion to the left of the mid line now measures 4.8 x 4.2 x
5.2 cms and appears somewhat smaller than on the previous examination.
An area of para-aortic lymphadenopathy just beneath the renal hilum
now measures 1.6 cms in transverse diameter. Liver, kidneys and
spleen appear normal. There appears to have been some improvement
despite the lack of conventional treatment.

```
Referred: DR P. CLARKE                          DOB: 24 Apr 1953
          HAEMATOLOGY UNIT VOLDGH,MAIN ST.      PGE: 1
```

HISTORY:
NHL, on carrot diet!

CT ABDOMEN & PELVIS:
Despite the rather unconventional therapy Mrs Grout's mass continues
to get better! Today the Abdomen has been scanned in 10/15mm slices
without IV contrast. There is a single mass lesion at slice 2.15 with
measures 2.6 X 3.9cms. There is still localised adenopathy anterior
to the cava and inferior pole of right kidney. This has markedly
reduced in size. The only further adenopathy is a 1cm node lying to
the left of the aorta at slice 2.14. Overall there has been a
subjective remission of around 75%.

CONCLUSION:
Eats more vegetables!

VALE OF LEVEN X-RAY REPORT

Patient : CATHERINE GROUT   Status : OP   Reg: 232401
Referred: DR P. CLARKE   DOB: 24 Apr 1953
          HAEMATOLOGY UNIT VOLDGH,MAIN ST.   PGE: 1

HISTORY:
Lymphoma (treated by carrots)!

CT CHEST, ABDOMEN & PELVIS:
Yet again Mrs Grout continues to improve. The previously noted
adenopathy is now extremely difficult to define. There is still an
area of vague increased soft tissue density in the mid abdomen at the
site of the previous intermesenteric mass. Most of the other
adenopathy is barely disearnable. The features are further improved
and represent greater than 90% remission from the original scans.

HISTORY:
NHL.

ULTRASOUND OF ABDOMEN:
Normal liver, gallbladder, biliary tree, kidneys, spleen and
pancreas.

No adenopathy.

VALE OF LEVEN X-RAY REPORT

Patient : CATHERINE GROUT   Status : OP   Reg: 232401
Referred: DR P. CLARKE   DOB: 24 Apr 1953
          HAEMATOLOGY UNIT VOLDGH,MAIN ST.   PGE: 1

HISTORY
NHL 6 years ago.

UTRASOUND OF ABDOMEN
Normal liver, kidneys and spleen. Reasonable access to aorta and
iliac subtain. No recurrent adenopathy seen. Site of original lesion
in mid abdomen shows no evidence of recurrence.

A FEW SCARY PICTURES

"RABBITS DON'T GET LYMPHOMA!"

Part Two

CLEARING OUT
THE JUNK
ON ALL LEVELS

Chapter Six

WORDS OF CAUTION

I THOUGHT LONG AND HARD about whether to include a detailed account of the diet that helped me. I am only too aware that I bumbled my way back into health. And yet, in spite of my ignorance, I did find a way, or a combination of processes, that actually worked for me.

The diet was my first step and is an inescapable part of my recovery. It is of course, no "lymphoma bible". Nonetheless, it was my guiding light for the first two years.

I am sure some of you will read the recipes I followed and think 'Oh my God! She had yoghurt every day! But that's dairy, that's soooo *bad*,' or 'What, salmon three times a week? But salmon is so full of toxic metals. That's got to be a big no no!'

I have come across many different, and almost always contradictory, opinions about the best way to achieve and sustain recovery from a disease like cancer. Such contradictions are so confusing for those of us trying to find a way to get well again.

How do you choose? How can you possibly adopt the best approach for you? More importantly, how long do you go on searching before you start actually doing something?

Of course, research is completely necessary, whether you decide to explore conventional or alternative methods of treatment. Finding out more about the substances used in chemotherapy and their side-effects can be thought provoking, to put it mildly. It is also relevant when looking for alternative methods. So many Internet sites claim to have the perfect supplements to help various conditions that you could end up completely overwhelmed by the sheer abundance of information available on the web.

Yet **there are perfectly valid** (not to say, **superior**) **alternatives** to radiotherapy, chemotherapy and surgery. In truth, there are many different approaches that have been successful in bringing back health to people with cancer. There is the Gerson diet of course; the Grape Cure; Laetrile or B17; Essiac tea, a powerful body detoxifier that former nurse Renée Caisse used to cure countless people. More recently, Tullio Simoncini, an oncologist, found that cancerous tumours could be eradicated using a solution of bicarbonate of soda. Light Therapy is yet another method. I could go on… They are unfortunately rarely made public and when they are, it is usually with such a negative bias that they are discredited or ridiculed along with those who are 'misguided' enough to use them.

Anyone requiring proof of this need only read Breuss's own account of his struggle to get his approach officially recognised. You can feel his frustration at the establishment when he questions whether '45,000 successful cases are nothing'. Or read Max Gerson's story and see how he was vilified for also finding a treatment that actually worked beautifully. And did I mention that Dr. Simoncini is no longer able to practise in hospitals because he refused to continue using chemotherapy and radiotherapy? According to him these methods have too many dangerous side effects, do not work and cause too much pain.

I certainly knew nothing about alternative methods until I was diagnosed and finding out that such things were possible gave me tremendous hope. But for anyone trying to find the 'perfect' approach, let me make this really clear: there must come a time when research has to be put on hold and action has to be taken.

In her book *Why People Don't Heal And How They Can,* Caroline Myss states that 'healing' is 'a present time challenge'[3]. So, change has to become a friend and it has to happen **now**!

In my particular case, I can say that it took me a week of very intense, focused reading to get a feeling, an impulse, an intuition about what I wanted to do. A sudden enthusiasm seized me after reading Rudolph Breuss's book. Something spoke to me about his approach and I chose to listen. I started following his diet for leukaemia for a few weeks, even though I did not have this disease. It may not have been 'perfect' but it was something I felt drawn to.

So this is my first recipe - a bit of intense brain work followed by a period of assimilation of the information gathered. I would then recommend switching off the left brain, the rational part of us, to allow an acute awareness of the emotions, of the body's intuitive response to develop. In my case, in the space of a week, I learnt to undo all the years of not trusting my gut feeling and to give it the respect it deserves. Yes, I assure you, it can be done.

The second recipe embraces being flexible - just because you start with one approach does not mean that it cannot be refined along the way.

My experience showed me that once your intention is firmly set on doing whatever it takes to heal yourself, some very powerful 'coincidences' come into play and according to Bernie Siegel in his book *Peace, Love and Healing* they are 'God's way of remaining anonymous'[4]. Here is one among the many I have been blessed to experience: just as I was feeling that fresh vegetable juices would be preferable to the bottled ones I was using, Jan, a lovely colleague from school, happened to drop by. She had in her hands the very book I needed. It was called *Juicing for Life* by two renowned nutritionists, Cherie Calbom and Maureen Keane. It was to be another source of inspiration to me.

So, I quickly read the short chapter on cancer in their book. The list of known causes of cancer was very long indeed and according to the research they refer to, "80 to 90 percent of all cancers are environmentally related". I'll give you one guess which factor in this very broad category happens to be the number-one contributing factor? Yes, you've got it - diet. Basically the message was that you deprive your body of nutrient-rich foods at your own peril.

Juicing raw vegetables was an easy way to flood all body systems with more nutrients than you could possibly chomp your way through, or absorb, from eating them in their original state. The book also looked at cancer prevention and recommended drinking a pint of carrot juice a day as a very effective way to prevent this disease. I wished I had known that years ago, things might have been very different had I swapped my usual diet drinks laced with artificial sweeteners, for carrot juice.

When, much later, I told Dr. McGlinchey that I was getting through (with Ian's help) 15 kilos of carrots per week, he looked at me and chuckled, 'Now I know why rabbits don't get lymphoma!'

So, here is, for what it's worth, all that this little 'rabbit' did.

Chapter Seven

JUICE FOR YOUR LIFE

JUICING WAS SUCH A VITAL PART of my recovery that I have devoted a whole chapter to it. There are entire books on the subject, but let me tell you why I became convinced that juicing vegetables would be a good way to rid my body of cancer.

As I mentioned earlier, I read a lot after my initial diagnosis. Having found Rudolph Breuss's book on using vegetable juices and special herbal teas whetted my appetite for more. I bought Max Gerson's *A Cancer Therapy: Results of Fifty Cases*. The first thing I did was to look at the X-Ray photographs. The 'before' pictures were frightening, but the ones showing the results of the juices and diet spoke volumes. They imprinted on my brain as the visible proof that such almost miraculous recoveries were possible.

Most people who get cancer have many nutritional deficiencies. Their cells tend to be very acidic. Vegetable juicing is a fantastic way to give your body an abundance of the nutrients it needs in a way that requires minimum effort by your digestive system to assimilate. It is also a simple way to make your body more alkaline, and cancer cells cannot survive in an alkaline medium.

JUICERS

All juices are made by feeding the ingredients into a juicer so let's talk about *juicers*. I bought a Kenwood JE500 juicer the day before I started my diet. When I look at it now or use it, I cannot believe it has lasted so long, or that I managed to make so many juices with it every day. Mind you, there were times when I really got sick at the mere sight of it and others when I could have easily chucked it out of the window. It was far from the perfect juicer, but it got me through all the same.

It is sadly not performing so well now, but it is an old friend and I keep it, for sentimental reasons and for when I travel.

I have recently bought a bigger L'Equip juicer and find it more efficient when it comes to the quantity and quality of juice delivered by the same amount of raw produce.

Many juicing books recommend the Champion juicer. It does not use centrifugal force to extract the juice and this is considered better for those who are intent on getting maximum nutrition from the juices. Apparently, many of the beneficial enzymes may be destroyed by the heat generated in a centrifugal juicer. This is debatable and all I can say is, it still worked for me.

If you are reading this and think that juicing is something you may want to try, my advice would be to make sure that, no matter which type you decide to buy, it can cope with juicing hard root vegetables as well as delicate green leaves. In addition, it should be able to juice a large quantity of raw produce without having to either scrape clean or empty the basket all the time. A big enough feeder to allow large carrots and the like to go through would also be helpful as you do not want to spend too much time cutting the ingredients into ridiculously small pieces. Life is too short.

You can keep the pulp from most juices and use it in soups, salads etc. I usually just put it on the compost heap. After emptying the juicer, I simply rinse the removable parts under a cold tap. Very soon, I stopped trying to clean those parts back to their original colour. No matter what I did, the plastic and metal parts in contact with the vegetables always turned brown. Later, I experimented with Ecover bleach and very hot water. I clean my juicer quite regularly with this method and it works a treat, provided you soak the different parts long enough and use a stiff brush to give them a good scrape now and again.

MY JUICING RITUAL

The recommended amount for each juice is about six fluid ounces.

I must confess that mine tended to be much larger, in fact they were between 12 and 14 fl oz. I did warn you, I allowed my intuition to take over and this amount felt right for me.

Before juicing the vegetables, I removed all blemishes, of

course, and then I usually just scrubbed them well in cold, **filtered** water. I didn't peel them because a lot of the nutritional value is found just under the surface of the skin. I used only **organic** produce since I was trying to minimise my exposure to harmful chemicals. I also drank the juices freshly made to maximise their nutritional content.

As I was making them and drinking them, I made sure that **I kept foremost in my mind all the wonderful properties each ingredient had**. For instance, a lot of these juices contain carrot juice which is full of betacarotene. Beta-carotene has been found to fight all sorts of cancers, including non-Hodgkin's lymphoma.

As I cut the carrots, I would really focus on their colour and say to myself, '**This is packed with beta-carotene. My tumours** (I called them tumours because enlarged lymph nodes was too long but I knew what I meant) **really don't stand a chance'** or '**Carrots, the number one cancer-fighting, liver-cleansing vegetable,'** and so on with each ingredient. This was my own take on visualisation and affirmation principles and I am 100 percent sure that the healing power of these juices was multiplied by this little ritual.

After a while, I did not have to say the words or even think them. I could 'feel' the powerful ingredients with each sip and imagine my cells vibrating with joy, all over my body.

The juices represented most, if not all my fluid intake.

I did have some water and various herbal teas as well. I also kept taking the sage tea and kidney tea from Rudolph Breuss's regime for the first year.

JUICE RECIPES

1 ~ Cherie's Cleansing Cocktail

This is the juice I had most mornings before breakfast. It contains beetroot, a very powerful liver and blood cleanser and ginger which has anti-inflammatory properties. It also helps cleanse the lymph. Use **raw beetroot**, not pickled or cooked.

1 small raw beetroot (5 or 6ozs)
About $1/4$ inch piece of fresh ginger root,
1 small eating apple or $1/2$ a large one.
Include the pips as they contain vitamin B17,
 a powerful tumour eradicator also found in
 apricot kernels and almonds.
4 carrots with green tops removed.
(Cherie Calbom does not recommend using the pips from the apple in Juicing for Life, *this is my own addition.)*

I would quite often use much more ginger than this, as I absolutely love it. I also loved to see the reaction on Ian's face as he drank his first couple of mouthfuls and then, eyes moistened by the liquid fire, he would exclaim 'Wow, a bit powerful today!'

Let me share another anecdote regarding this juice. My friend Stephanie became quite interested in juicing after seeing what it had done for me. She thought that this juice in particular, sounded really delicious. Now, Stephanie, a girl after my own heart, does not usually do things by half. Instead of using a small beetroot, she decided to add a whole enormous one to her juice (in for a penny, in for a pound, she thought). She felt so nauseous that she had to spend the whole day in bed, with a bucket by the side of it!

2 ~ Garden Salad Special

This juice contains garlic - one clove only. **Beware**, a little goes a long way. Don't use any more than this. Garlic is a phenomenal immune system booster when consumed raw. It has been proven to destroy cancer cells in test tubes. Broccoli is also a well-known cancer fighting vegetable.

3 broccoli florets
1 garlic clove
4 to 5 carrots or 2 tomatoes
2 large stalks of celery
$1/2$ a green pepper

The reason I put a warning about the garlic is that one clove may appear to be a pitiful amount. A young man of my acquaintance, also keen on juicing, thought that a clove meant a whole head of garlic and juiced the lot. Thank God he only took one tiny mouthful, because he spent the best part of a day bent over a sink, frothing at the mouth like a dog with rabies!

3 ~ Garlic Express

This juice contains ingredients that boost potassium levels. Potassium should be plentiful inside healthy cells. It helps to remove excess sodium and restores balance within.

A handful of parsley (with stalks if possible)
1 garlic clove
4 to 5 carrots
2 large stalks of green celery
Juice the parsley, and celery together first to make the most of the parsley. Then add garlic and finally the carrots.

4 ~ Alkaline Special

Excellent for making the body more alkaline, a condition that is required for healing.

1/4 head of red or green cabbage
3 stalks of celery

❖   ❖   ❖

5 ~ Calcium-rich Cocktail

This juice is high in absorbable calcium, among other things.

3 kale leaves with stalks
A small handful of parsley
4 to 5 carrots
$^1/_2$ an apple
The kale leaves do not yield much juice neither does the parsley so I tried to juice those two ingredients together with the apple, followed by the carrots.

6 ~ Cantaloupe Shake

This is again a rich source of beta-carotene. It is an ideal mid-afternoon drink, as a special treat.

$^1/_2$ a cantaloupe melon or any orange-fleshed melon, with skin on. Cut into strips and juice.
It could not be simpler. You can add mineral water to dilute the sugar content. I did not have this one very often, only when I fancied something sweet.

7 ~ Chlorophyll Cocktail

A handful of parsley
4 carrots
A handful of spinach
$^1/_2$ an apple
It should have a handful of beetroot tops as well but I

never managed to get beetroot with the leaves left on, so I just used a bit more spinach. When chard was in season, I would use it too. I even added fresh nettles in the spring for good measure. It is well worth getting beetroot tops as they are one of the best liver cleansers.

To make the most of the parsley and beetroot tops, if you are lucky enough to get them, wrap them inside the spinach and process first. Then add the apple and finally the carrots.

8 ~ Potassium Broth

A Handful of parsley
A handful of spinach
4-5 carrots without leaves
2 stalks of green celery
Bunch up parsley and spinach leaves, and push through with carrots and celery.

9 ~ Ginger Hopper

This final drink contains ginger - high in antioxidants and in cancer-fighting properties.

$1/4$ to $1/2$ inch of fresh root ginger
4 to 5 carrots
$1/2$ an apple
I would also add raw celery to this a lot of the time.

Chapter Eight

MY REGIME

For the first couple of months, I followed the Breuss diet for Leukaemia.

First thing in the morning, I would drink slowly half a cup of cold kidney tea (this tea is to be drunk for three weeks only, then after a period of 2 -3 weeks it can be taken again if needed).

Half an hour later, I would have 1or 2 cups of warm sage tea, made according to his recipe.

During the day, I would eat a relatively normal diet but no pork or beef. I had by then removed sugar and convenience foods of all kinds from my diet. I would also drink 1/4 litre of bottled Biotta Breuss juice. This had to be sipped slowly, before meals. I would have another cup of kidney tea before lunch and a final one just before going to bed. During the day I would also take a cup of cold cranesbill tea.

Then, once I decided that fresh juices would be even more beneficial, this is the kind of regime I followed. (I kept the sage tea, kidney tea and cranesbill tea for a year after switching to fresh juices).

Breakfast:

Juice

Fruit *(raw or cooked)*

Wholegrain cereals *(I usually had porridge)*.

    Hot or cold, with rice milk or almond milk.

1 cup of green tea

Mid-morning snack:

Juice

Lunch:

Juice

Salad of leafy greens with a clove of garlic and lemon juice or organic cider vinegar and olive oil dressing or soup/broth or sandwich/ *(I made my own wholewheat bread in those days!)* or homemade houmous.

Herbal tea

I could have eaten all of the above if I'd wanted but I never managed it. I mostly had an enormous salad with lots of bits and pieces. I have included the recipe in this book.

Mid-afternoon snack:

Juice

Yoghurt (plain, live full-fat or low-fat, organic)

I started with low fat and moved on to full fat within the first year.

Dinner:

Juice

Cold-water fish / Organic chicken (Steamed, boiled or baked) with steamed vegetables and brown rice.
I would also have beans and brown rice with vegetables and various vegetable casseroles and soups, all home made of course.

Evening snack:

Juice

I always added a drizzle, or, if I'm completely honest, a 'downpour' of olive oil to my vegetables and I used lots of herbs and masses of raw or cooked garlic.
Cheeky Graham used to tell me as he was giving me some Reiki, that I reminded him of a lovely roast leg of lamb because the smell of garlic was oozing out of my pores! This just goes to show that ridicule does not kill you.

Another important aspect of my regime was the type of food I had to abstain from. My beloved cheese became a thing of the past, for instance. When I was in France, cheese had always been my favourite part of a meal. I would often pinch some before we sat down to eat, to ensure I had enough room for it. My mum would usually catch me, red-handed, shout and be generally appalled by my behaviour.

Just to make it absolutely crystal clear, these are the kinds of foods that I cut out completely from my diet –

all processed foods, convenience foods, white flour, sugar, especially white refined sugar, foods containing hydrogenated vegetable oil (all margarines and so-called 'healthy' spreads for instance and biscuits to name but two items on this very long list), chocolate, dairy products (except organic live yoghurt), meat (beef and pork especially. Goodbye lovely bacon!), table salt, alcohol, fizzy drinks of any kind, coffee, tea (except for one cup of green tea a day), additives of any kind, artificial sweeteners including aspartame - look out for it as it has many different brand names.

The way I cooked also changed radically. Gone were my delicious béchamel sauces and sautéed potatoes. I invested in a steamer and steamed, briefly, all the vegetables that I did not eat raw. I would also steam fish or chicken in nice little greaseproof paper 'papillottes'(parcels). I tried to keep saturated fat content to a minimum but did add extra-virgin, cold-pressed, organic olive oil to my food just before eating it.

I included the following in my diet:

1 serving = 1/2 cup of whole produce

Wholewheat (mostly as my homemade bread - only about one slice a day), brown rice, millet, buckwheat groats, quinoa, steamed/baked potatoes, 2 to 5 servings a day.

Beans 3 to 5 cups a week.
For strict vegetarians, the recommended amounts are more substantial, 2 to 3 cups a day. I tended to use mostly chick peas, mung beans and aduki beans as I found all beans quite hard to digest, if you know what I mean? Yes, I do mean the 'fart' factor!

Nuts and seeds 1 to 2 servings a day.
I kept mine in the fridge to ensure that they did not go rancid. I avoided peanuts and peanut butter (they contain harmful aflatoxins) and learnt to appreciate other nut butters like almond and cashew.

Vegetables 4 to 8 servings a day
Especially nice green lettuce of all sorts
(but not iceberg: not green enough), cabbage, kale, carrot, butternut squash, green pepper, spinach, spring greens, garlic, broccoli, cauliflower, root ginger, beetroot, sprouted seeds and sprouted beans/lentils.

Fruit 2 to 4 servings a week
Especially apples, pineapples, blueberries, grapes, cantaloupes.

Live organic low-fat yoghurt was recommended but I quite often substituted it with the **full-fat** version.

Organic poultry 3 to 4 ozs per serving

Seafood:
I ate a lot of fish and also some shellfish. Langoustines were a rare but oh so enjoyable treat. I learnt to appreciate fresh oily fish of many kinds - mackerel, sardines, herring, and salmon *(not smoked)*.
I discovered that the Loch Fyne Oyster bar in Clachan, near Inveraray, would deliver very nice farmed salmon, reared in clear waters with strong currents and not fed full of antibiotics and other horrors. More recently, I have been able to get some organic fresh salmon from my local fishmongers.

Regarding fats, the ones allowed in this diet were extra-virgin, cold-pressed, organic olive oil, and flaxseed oil which is fantastic for its Omega 3 content. Use it on cereals in the morning, for example, or drizzle on salads and food once it has cooled a little. You must **never** cook with it, it's a very unstable oil. Nowadays I tend to use coconut oil for cooking anything that requires a high temperature.

I have included a few of my favourite recipes for you to try at home.
Only use **organic** ingredients.

❀ ❀ ❀

SOUPS

Wild rice soup

4 to 5 sticks celery, washed and cut into small pieces
1.5 litres homemade vegetable stock for extra flavour
    or water
2 tablespoons extra-virgin olive oil
1 large onion, red if possible, chopped
50g short-grain brown rice, washed and drained
30g wild rice
Sea-salt (optional) and black pepper, freshly milled
2 tablespoons fresh coriander, finely chopped
(or parsley. Fresh French tarragon is also delicious)

Put olive oil in a deep pan and turn heat on very low. Add onion and sweat gently until it is soft and translucent. Do not let the onion brown, whatever you do.
Add rice and stir around for about a minute. Then add celery, stock and seasoning. Bring to the boil, cover, turn the heat down and simmer on a very low heat for about 35 minutes or until rice is cooked.
You can eat it like this, chunky, or put it in a food processor if you like a smoother soup.
Add the chopped, fresh herbs at the last minute.

❊   ❊   ❊

Potassium-Rich Vegetable Broth

This vegetable broth, from Cherie Calbom, John Calbom and Michael Mahaffey's book, *The complete cancer cleanse*[5] provides important minerals that your body needs during a cleansing process. Eat 1 or 2 cups of the broth daily.

2 to 3 cups chopped fresh green beans
2 to 3 cups chopped courgettes
2 to 3 stalks celery
1 cup coarsely chopped onion
1 to 3 tablespoons chopped parsley
1 tablespoon chopped garlic

Steam the green beans, courgettes, celery and onion over filtered water until soft, but still green and not mushy. Place the cooked vegetables, plus the raw parsley and garlic, in a blender and puree until smooth. Add a bit of the steaming water, as needed, but keep the broth fairly thick. Season to taste with grated ginger, cayenne pepper, vegetable seasoning, or herbs of your choice.

❊   ❊   ❊

A FEW FAVOURITE RECIPES

Houmous

This is such a nutritious dish and is so delicious that I still make it all the time. I try to always use dried chickpeas, soaked overnight. The taste is far superior and they are much better for you than the tinned ones. Cooking the chickpeas with several cloves of garlic and some root ginger will also help 'de-gas' them, you know what I mean. Changing the water after it has boiled for three minutes or soaking in water for longer will further reduce this unfortunate side effect.

125g dried, soaked chickpeas -
    cook for about 1.5 to 2 hours.
Juice of 2 to 3 lemons depending on size
3 tablespoons light tahini paste
2 to 3 garlic cloves, according to taste.
    Crush before putting in the blender
Sea-salt/Herbamare salt (optional)
1 tablespoon extra-virgin olive oil and 1 tablespoon
water *(or 2 of olive oil if you are not worried about calories)*
Pinch of cayenne pepper

Put the chickpeas, tahini paste and lemon juice into a blender or food processor. Add salt (if used), crushed garlic and cayenne pepper. Finally add olive oil/water to achieve the desired consistency. Taste and decide if it needs more lemon, salt etc.

Spoon the contents into a bowl, cover with film and chill. I like to serve this with celery sticks, carrots, cucumber and warm pitta bread.

ENJOY!

Broccoli in garlic

This is a delicious way of barely cooking your broccoli. It is a great side dish and goes well with fish, chicken, or just about anything.

For two people:
1 small to medium head of broccoli
2 large cloves of garlic
Olive oil
Cover the bottom of a medium saucepan with a little water (filtered if possible). Cut broccoli into medium-sized florets taking care to remove the hard outside skin. Add the stalk too, peeled, so that you only use the white part cut into smallish chunks. Add the chopped garlic.

Heat the saucepan on high heat for about 3 minutes or until all the water has evaporated. Then add a drizzle *(you know by now what my take on 'drizzle' is, don't you?)* of olive oil, salt and pepper if required and serve. Delicious.

Cathie's Salad

For one person:

1 small lettuce (batavia is wonderful if you can get it)
2 to 3 broccoli florets, taken apart *(by this I mean picking tiny florets from each piece. If this is too time consuming, just cut the florets into smaller pieces, lengthwise)*
1 fat clove of garlic chopped finely
1/2 a ripe avocado
3/4 cocktail tomatoes or 1 medium tomato cut into
    pieces
3/4 dried, unsulphured apricots cut into small pieces.
A good handful of coriander leaves finely chopped.
1 tablespoon each of sunflower seeds and pumpkin seeds soaked in water overnight.

For the dressing:

I like to make my own dressing and keep it in an old jam jar. Before serving I give it a good shake and use about 1 tablespoon per portion.
You will need:
1 teaspoon Dijon mustard
Extra-virgin olive oil
Cider vinegar *(only cider vinegar is acceptable when trying to rid oneself of cancer)*
Sea salt/Herbamare salt and pepper to taste
Dried/fresh herbs (optional)/cayenne pepper (optional) /garlic (optional)

Put Dijon mustard into a jam jar. Add cider vinegar, enough to fill about half the jar *(less if you do not want the dressing to be too strong)*. Add salt and pepper to taste *(remember that salt is optional and should only be used very sparingly)*. Put the lid on firmly and shake the jar vigorously for a few seconds. This helps to dissolve the salt thoroughly. Add olive oil and fill to just under the lid. Add remaining ingredients. If you like the taste of dried/fresh French tarragon, you can add about 1 dessertspoon to the mixture. Shake and serve. Keep the jar the fridge.

To assemble the salad:
First, place the dressing at the bottom of the bowl (you may wish to add cayenne pepper for a bit of 'heat')
Add the chopped garlic, apricots, broccoli florets, avocado, and tomatoes. Then, place the lettuce leaves on top and toss. Just before serving, add the seeds and chopped coriander.
This makes a lovely, filling lunch.
You can add other ingredients like chopped celery, grated beetroot or carrot, red pepper, green pepper, grated cabbage. Just use your imagination.

Chapter Nine

SIDE EFFECTS

A COUPLE OF MONTHS into my 'extreme juicing' regime, my skin turned quite orange, as though I had applied fake tan with a heavy hand. This was due to beta-carotene being stored in my tissues. I read this was quite harmless, so I wasn't worried and later on, when I developed a rash on my abdomen those same books made me realise that this could be part of the healing process, a manifestation of toxicity being released through the skin. So I did not try to make the rash disappear - I welcomed its presence as confirmation that my body was ridding itself of years of accumulated 'gunk'.

What was more distressing for a woman like me (i.e. vain) were the peculiar spots that adorned my chin for many months. They looked like funny little (and some not so little) white pyramids. However, I sensed that they were caused by the disintegration of my tumours and meant my immune system was doing its job. So I learnt to accept them with good humour. I was feeling so good by then that nothing could have stopped me.

However, I was scared when my right breast developed a so-called 'fibrocystic' condition roughly two months after I started juicing. I rushed to the breast clinic to be told, after an extremely painful mammogram and a needle aspiration of the lump that the condition was benign and that in any case, there was nothing they could do.

As you can imagine, this lack of explanation left me rather perplexed. I also suspected that my new regime had somehow caused this to happen, but why?

I have since learnt that vegetables such as broccoli and other members of the cabbage family, if eaten raw in large quantities, can depress the action of the thyroid gland and this can have a direct impact on breast tissue. The same goes for soya. I was eating rather a lot of both when I first changed my diet, driven as I was by my usual 'all or nothing' Taurean attitude. If certain foods had cancer-fighting properties, surely, the more I ate of them the better?

I also suspect that my thyroid had been struggling for many years without me realising it. I remember that my eyes always looked very large and bulged somewhat, another indication of thyroid distress.

Now, let me share something else with you, something I have learnt since going on this juicing diet. According to Dr. Max Gerson, because juicing is such a powerful way to detoxify all your systems, the body's eliminatory organs may become overwhelmed by the released poisons. In fact, some of Max Gerson's own early patients died of hepatic coma during their experimental treatment. It was only after he introduced coffee enemas to his regime that Max Gerson was able to avoid this fatal liver overload.

'Damn it' I did no such enemas! The logical not to say worrying, conclusion is that I should be dead... What can account for the fact that I am still around? Well, for one thing, I kept taking the sage and kidney teas from Rudolph Breuss's diet for a whole year. These teas are powerful and, according to the mysterious 'Dr. Med F B from Berchtes-gaden', in an appendix to Breuss's book[6], they help put the 'disturbed metabolic system' back in order.

Furthermore, I was walking everyday and sweated my way to many hilltops I can tell you. A lot of toxicity is removed from the body through intense physical exercise and the perspiration it produces. The lungs also expel many toxins via the breath and boy, was I breathing hard as I resolutely toiled up to the cairn!

On a different level, the very act of reaching the top filled me with a great sense of achievement and the beauty of the scenery that unfolded before my eyes made every fibre of my being connect with it. I felt such joy such bliss even, that it must have been like an injection of sunshine into the darkness that dwelt within my cells

My skin, as you know, took over some of the elimination and I felt that the orange hue in my complexion was also due partly to an excess of toxins which had been stored there for a while.

I believe that reflexology also helped me cope with the increased toxic load my body had to process, but I also now feel that I might not have been quite so orange nor would I have overloaded my lymph so much had I done some coffee enemas, as per Max Gerson's recommendations. What more can I say, you live and learn!

Three years later, after studying with the inspirational Barbara Wren at the College of Natural Nutrition, I realised that my lymphatic system had been struggling virtually from day one and started doing coffee enemas along with many other detoxifying techniques.

It's never too late to learn.

Chapter Ten

EATING OUT

EATING OUT and being invited to dinner by friends was indeed a challenge. I found it best to let friends and family know what I was doing, exactly. Soon, people got used to my funny ways and stopped asking me questions. Some even took the challenge enthusiastically and tried to source organic produce for me, others could not, and that was also fine with me. I usually cooked something for myself and took it along with me.

Restaurants were more difficult. A few provide organic produce and, if you trust the chef, you can always ask him or her to cook your food the way you want it. Personally, I did not eat out much during the first two years, but that was my choice.

Another challenge was visiting my family in France. This required extensive homework prior to departure to ensure that there was a steady supply of organic produce available locally. For several years I travelled with a suitcase that I had labelled 'VEG', with enough vegetables or some bottled Breuss juice to last me a few days, just in case.

Once I was stopped at Glasgow Airport and had my hand luggage searched. As luck would have it, this was the only time I was carrying some carrots in my rucksack, along with my juicer. It was around Christmas and I had run out of room in my suitcase because it was full of presents. The attendant's mouth fell open at the sight of my juicer. I tried to explain, but he couldn't even understand the concept of vegetable juicing. He looked very suspiciously at the juicer and stopped just short of plugging it in, to check whether it was real. He asked me to open the plastic bag containing my carrots. I suppose they must have looked suspiciously like sticks of dynamite on the X-ray machine. He looked at the carrots, then at me from head to toe and asked 'You always travel with your carrots, madam?' I was about to give him a stern lecture on the benefits of juicing vegetables when you had cancer, when I noticed the twinkle in his eyes.

Needless to say, I don't do this anymore, organic vegetables are a lot easier to find. It's probably just as well, as I cannot imagine, in our current climate of fear and suspicion, getting through any airport security checks with such dangerous weapons as raw carrots!

...And Another Thing

This cleansing diet has to be adhered to religiously for some time to make sure there is no recurrence of the cancer. In accordance with Max Gerson's recommendations about his own protocol, I followed this diet quite rigidly for *two years* and then progressively reduced the amount of juicing I was doing.

For a couple of years after that, my maintenance program was three juices per day, one before each meal. It is only in the last year or so that I have reduced this amount further and have now decided to 'play it by ear'.

I still eat mainly organic food and have a big salad most lunchtimes but I have relaxed to the point where I do allow myself some 'forbidden foods' now and again. There is of course the odd occasion when I still feel the compulsion to reach for 'comfort foods'. The difference is that these instances are now few and far between and usually occur when I am stressed or tired and have allowed the frenetic pace of life to get on top of me. So instead of giving myself a hard time at my lack of self-control, I try to find out the cause of it. Sometimes, it is just that, a temporary imbalance due to having too much to do and not having taken the time to look after myself properly. This is usually quite easy to remedy once the crisis is over, with increased juicing and regular exercise outdoors. There are times however when I need to look deeper for an explanation: what deep and dark emotion lurks within me that needs to be smothered in Green and Black's chocolate, what hurt needs to be buried under an avalanche of all butter shortbread? You see I have learnt not to allow these emotions to remain within me unexpressed, unchallenged or unexplained. Facing up to them and trying to achieve some form of inner peace by letting go of them is a painful struggle, but when I occasionally succeed I feel another piece of my heart open up.

One of the drawbacks of this regime is that you can become quite paranoid about food. I certainly found certain times of the year very challenging, so adamant was I that not a morsel of non-organic food would pass my lips. I remember driving for miles around one Christmas time, frantically looking for organic vegetables in various supermarkets. The company that usually delivered my weekly orders was enjoying a well-earnt break but I was left in a panic over where to find all the fresh ingredients for my juices. This was ten years ago and organic vegetables were not as common as they are now.

With time, I understood that it was not just my food that was healing my cancer, but also my renewed connection to my true self and the purpose of my life. As a consequence, I became a little more adventurous, a little less reluctant to travel. Nowadays I no longer fret at the thought of eating 'the right food' when I am on holiday somewhere, I just make the most of whatever fresh local food there is and have the best of times.

Chapter Eleven

WHAT ABOUT SUPPLEMENTS?

PEOPLE HAVE ASKED ME whether I took any supplements during those first few years. I only ever took about 100mg of zinc and the same amount of vitamin B6, as well as a high dose multi B vitamin capsule. I also took Echinacea drops daily to help support and boost my immune system.

About seven years ago, after studying with the College of Natural Nutrition, I learnt how to put into practice the wonderfully empowering philosophy of this college. I started taking flax oil, lecithin granules, magnesium citrate, a good antioxidant capsule and a supplement called Supamag which contains many of the vitamins and minerals required to successfully break down and utilise the Omega 3 essential fatty acids in flax oil. I still take flax oil daily and fish oils, especially in the winter months. I have also learnt about the body's need for iodine. It is especially necessary for women as it protects breast tissue. I take it in the form of Lugol's solution.

I regularly work with certain naturopathic techniques of detoxification such as castor oil packing, enemas of all kinds, hot tubbing and Epsom salt baths. I have even brushed aside my initial reluctance and discovered the amazing benefits of urine rubs and packs. Yes, you read that correctly. Swiftly moving on... In other words, I keep learning about new ways to detoxify the body and experimenting. This is an endless and exciting process.

I still read avidly and any information that helps me piece together the causes of my particular cancer fascinates me. I found an interesting article written by Pat Thomas in *What Doctors Don't Tell You* (WDDTY) and on their website www.wddty.com. WDDTY is a monthly health report which critically reviews issues related to both conventional and alternative medicine and it is a great source of information.

The title of the article already gives a clue as to the potential causes of this disease: *Non-Hodgkin's lymphoma - A cry for help from a polluted body.* The piece concludes:

> *'From an holistic point of view, NHL is best described as a cry for help from a polluted body. All the available evidence suggests that, to reduce the risk of developing NHL and to fight it once it occurs, taking multiple actions to detoxify our environments both inside and outside the body may be the most positive and productive way to deal with this renegade cancer.'*

How amazing, I thought, that my intuition had guided me to do exactly that. As the next chapter will demonstrate, I too decided early on in my quest for health to reduce my exposure to toxicity of all kinds. I took many steps to clear my immediate environment, namely my house, of as many toxic substances as I could.

Chapter Twelve

OUT WITH TOXIC CHEMICALS!

I CHOSE AN ORGANIC DIET to remove potential toxicity from pesticides and other harmful substances, but I soon realised that many everyday products, supposed to be helpful or even 'natural', contained a cocktail of dangerous additives and preservatives.

I could not believe it. They were everywhere: in my shampoo and hair dye (yes, more vanity), in my make-up, deodorant and all my so-called 'beauty' products. Washing powders and house cleaning products were also riddled with them. I even found that my cooking utensils were not as innocent as they seemed.

Enraged by this discovery, I promptly cleared my cupboards of all the offending articles. When I saw how many there were and later on, when I understood how few of these supposed 'essential' products I really needed, I felt really stupid. How could I have allowed myself to get brainwashed into buying such dangerous rubbish?

Now, I am more philosophical and I just say to myself: "Live and learn, girl, live and learn." So, to help you do both, here are a few of the culprits masquerading as beneficial substances:

In toothpaste and some mouthwashes, **fluoride** is supposed to protect our teeth from dental cavities. 'Pah,' I say. It is actually a widely used insecticide and an acknowledged poison. Could this be why you must be careful not to put more than a pea-sized dollop of it on your toothbrush?

Here is what Dr. Joseph Mercola has to say on the matter:

'Fluoride accumulates in our bones, making them brittle and more easily fractured... accumulates in your pineal gland, which may inhibit the production of the hormone melatonin. Melatonin helps regulate the onset of puberty. Fluoride damages tooth enamel (known as dental fluorosis) and may lower fertility rates... has been found to increase the uptake of aluminium into your brain and lead into your blood. Fluoride inhibits antibodies from forming in your blood... confuses the immune system, causing it to attack the tissues in your body. This can increase the growth rate of tumours in people prone to cancer.' [7]

For those of you who are not familiar with Dr. Mercola, his journey from conventional medical training, from a doctor whose total belief that drugs had the power to cure all disease, to the realisation that a much more natural approach using diet was infinitely superior, is truly fascinating. His website (*www.mercola.com*) and daily newsletters are dedicated to 'educating others about taking back their health with natural medicine'.

Dr. Mercola would tell you that a much better way to keep your teeth from rotting is to eliminate refined sugar from your food.

Also found in toothpaste, **sodium lauryl/laureth sulfate** is a known irritant and potential carcinogenic best avoided. It is in shampoos, shower gels and countless other beauty products as well.

Most toothpastes and mouthwashes also use **saccharin** or some such artificial sweetener (sorbitol, xylitol, manitol and cyclamates). Saccharin is actually carcinogenic in large amounts, and these additives are not only unnecessary for tooth cleaning, but can also cause bloating and cramping if ingested.

I have found fennel toothpaste from Green People that suits me fine and it contains none of these 'nasties'.

The best way to keep our teeth clean is to invest in a good toothbrush and to brush for a lot longer than we actually do. About 2 minutes should do it.

Next on my hit list is **antiperspirant**. This item no longer has a place on my bathroom shelves. This product is full of aluminium. It has been linked to breast cancer and some suspect it might also be implicated in the development of Alzheimer's. Actually, antiperspirants are not a good idea. As you know, we eliminate a lot of toxins through sweat so it does not make sense to try and stop this natural and vital process from taking place.

If you think that even using a **deodorant** is okay because it only removes or more likely just masks, the smell of sweat, think again. Pat Thomas tells us in *Cleaning Yourself to Death*[8] (how is that for a cheery title?) that both antiperspirants and deodorants contain harmful chemicals such as:

stearyl alcohol and **parfum** (skin irritants),

polyethylene glycol (PEG compounds can be contaminated with the carcinogen 1,4-dioxane),

PPG-14 butyl ether (skin irritant and poisonous in high concentrations),

dibutylphthalate (hormone disrupting chemical implicated in reproductive abnormalities).

For added 'protection' some deodorants contain the antibacterial agent **triclosan**. This substance has been shown to cause liver damage in animals.

Should you wish to use a very natural alternative to a deodorant, apparently a dusting of plain cornstarch under the arms does a great job or you could always use a mixture of witch hazel, vegetable glycerine and various essential oils. Do not use **talcum powder** as an alternative to cornstarch. It is carcinogenic.

I avoided, and still avoid the following like the plague:

Propyl paraben and all the **parabens**. They are synthetic preservatives and unfortunately, easily absorbed. They are skin irritants and worse, oestrogen mimics.

Propylene glycol, in make-up and beauty products of all

kinds. It is a poisonous eye and skin irritant and also enhances the penetration of other more toxic chemicals.

PCBs (polychlorinated biphenyls) found in detergents, flame retardants, plastics and insulation materials. Hair sprays also contain them. Research has found significantly higher concentrations of these biphenyls in the blood of non-Hodgkin's lymphoma sufferers.

Benzene (chemically similar to Lindale and DDT) is another toxin linked to non-Hodgkin's lymphoma. It is found in a huge range of everyday products, from toothpaste and breakfast cereals to bottled water and lubricated condoms.

Chemical hair dyes are another way toxic products get into your bloodstream. I switched to henna instead after finding out that my particular type of cancer has been associated with **para-phenylenediamines**, an ingredient in some hair dyes I had used. In fact, some researchers believe that hair dyes may account for as many as 20 percent of non-Hodgkin's lymphoma cases in women.

Sun creams also are not all they are cracked up to be. I tend not to use them at all and wear long sleeves and a hat if I am going to be in the sun all day. According to the technical literature available, some sunscreen ingredients absorb into the blood and some are linked to toxic effects. Some release skin-damaging free radicals in sunlight, some act like oestrogen and could disrupt hormone systems, several are strongly linked to allergic reactions and still others may build up in the body or the environment.

Sunscreens also contain cancer-causing **Oxybenzone**, fragrance chemicals and numerous petrochemical-derived synthetic substances that actually promote cancer.

Another way these creams and sprays can be harmful is that their use prevents the skin from absorbing sunlight. This process is crucial to the body's ability to manufacture vitamin D. Sunscreen use **causes chronic deficiency** in the levels of this vitamin, leaving those who use them susceptible to depression, prostate cancer, breast cancer, osteoporosis and all the other degenerative health conditions caused by a lack of vitamin D. Furthermore, the use of vitamin D in the treatment of cancer has recently been proven to be highly beneficial.

So 'ditch' the creams and drink the 'veggies'! I am not joking, apparently broccoli extract works better as a sunscreen! And I can vouch for my lovely carrot juice of course.

Seriously though, the John Hopkins School of Medicine has found that an extract made from broccoli sprouts and smeared onto human skin boosts the body's natural ability to defend against ultraviolet solar rays that cause skin cancer. It is all to do with a substance they call Sulforaphane.

But don't take my word for it. You can check the veracity of all the above on the NaturalNews website. The editor of this newsletter is another of those modern 'knights in

shining armour' who endeavour to enlighten us regarding many health issues. This particular article on Sulphoraphane can be found on:
www.NaturalNews.com/023250_broccoli_cancer_sunscreen.html

For those of you who want to know more about the potential lethal side effects of some **additives** commonly found in our so-called beauty products, here is an extract from an article by Pat Thomas:

'Some of the most dangerous chemicals we put on our bodies in the name of beauty belong to a family of hormone disrupting chemicals, which are water soluble ammonia derivatives. DEA (diethanolamine), TEA (triethanolamine) and MEA (monoethanolamine) are almost always in products that foam: bubble bath, body washes, shampoos, soaps and facial cleansers. They are used to thicken, wet, alkalise and clean. While they are irritating to the skin, eyes and respiratory tract (Rev Environ Contam Toxicol, 1997; 149: 1-86), DEA, MEA and TEA are not considered particularly toxic in themselves. However, once added to the product, these chemicals readily react with any nitrites present to form potentially carcinogenic nitrosamines, such as NDEA (N-nitrosodiethanolamine). Of the three, MEA and DEA pose the greatest risk to human health. Prolonged exposure to these can alter liver and kidney function (J Am Coll Toxicol, 1983; 2: 183-235) and even lead to cancer (Rev Environ

Contam Toxicol, 1997; 149: 1-86).

'Nitrites get into personal care products in several ways. They can be added as anti corrosive agents, they can be released as a result of the degradation of other chemicals, specifically 2-nitro-1,3-propanediol (BNDP), or they can be present as contaminants in raw materials. Ingredients such as formaldehyde or formaldehyde forming chemicals, or 2-bromo-2-nitropropane (also known as bronopol) which can break down into formaldehyde, can also produce nitrosamines.*

'The long shelf life of most toiletries also increases the risk of creating a carcinogenic chemical reaction. Stored for a long time at elevated temperatures, nitrates will continue to form in a product, accelerated by the presence of certain other chemicals, such as formaldehyde, paraformaldehyde, thiocyanate, nitrophenols and certain metal salts (Science, 1973; 181: 1245-6; J Nat Cancer Inst, 1977; 58: 409; Nature, 1977; 266: 657-8; Fd Cosmet Toxicol, 1983; 21: 607-13).*

'Inadequate and confusing labelling means that consumers may never know which products are most likely to be contaminated. However, in a recent Food and Drug Administration (FDA) report, approximately **42 per cent of all cosmetics were contaminated with NDEA, with shampoos having the highest concentrations** (National Toxicology Program, Seventh Annual Report on Carcinogens, Rockville, MD: US Department of Health and Human Services, 1994...*

'*Manufacturers insist that DEA and its relatives are safe in products designed for brief or discontinuous use or those which wash off. However, there is evidence from both human and animal studies that NDEA can be quickly absorbed through the skin. (J Nat Cancer Inst, 1981; 66: 125-7; Toxicol Lett, 1979; 4: 217-22). This argument also doesn't explain why these chemicals crop up regularly in body lotions and facial moisturisers, which are of course* **meant to stay on the skin for long periods of time.** (my emphasis)

'*As far back as 1978, the International Agency for Research on Cancer (IARC) concluded that "although no epidemiological data were available, nitrosodiethanolamine should be regarded for practical purposes as if it were* **carcinogenic to humans**" *(IARC, 1978; 17: 77-82). This position was reaffirmed nearly 10 years later.*'

Scary, isn't it? To read the full article, go to www.wddty.com and type 'toxic toiletries' into the search engine.

Early on in my efforts to rid the house, and my body, of as many noxious compounds as I could, I stopped using **chlorine bleach**, a suspected carcinogen. In drinking water, it has been found to increase cancer risk in several studies.

Good quality drinking water is of paramount importance, whether we have a life-threatening condition or not. I am told that in Scotland, water used to taste lovely even if it looked a bit on the brown side due to peat sediment. However, nowadays, much more than harmless peat can be found in our drinking water. For instance, when we turn on a tap or flush the toilet, the first thing we notice is the unmistakable smell of chlorine. Worse still, some parts of the country have **fluoride** added to their tap water. And don't get me started on all the prescription drugs residue now found in our drinking water.

Soon after being diagnosed with cancer, I started using a jug with a charcoal cartridge to filter my drinking water. However, this only removes a small number of the potential pollutants in water so, a few years ago, I had a reverse osmosis system fitted under the kitchen sink. This seems to be one of the best methods of filtration. However, it is a good idea to take a good multi-mineral supplement if using this filtration method, as it also removes beneficial minerals from the water.

Apparently, according to Dr. Joseph Mercola and Dr. Kendra Pearsall[7] another way we expose ourselves to the damaging effects of **chlorine** is during a bath or shower. The skin absorbs it quite readily, so it might be worth investing in a whole-house filtering system or, at least, to fit the showerhead with a filtering unit. This is still but a dream of mine.

In the kitchen, after getting rid of my aluminium utensils, I threw away anything 'non-stick'. Teflon coating contains

PFOA (perfluorooctanoic acid), which has been implicated in pancreatic cancer, cancer of the testicles, breast cancer, thyroid problems etc. The list grows longer by the day.

More information is available on Dr. Mercola's website. This man never sleeps.

I also became aware of more sources of toxicity in some products that I had been using over the years, such as washing powders and fabric softeners. I experimented with eco-friendly washing powder, washing balls and soap nuts for my laundry. I gave up on commercial fabric softeners. Apparently borax can be used instead in the final rinse, but I never tried this out: we have very soft water here, in the west of Scotland, so I find there is no real need for this type of product.

I realised that my house too could be kept clean without all this chemical paraphernalia. Simple ingredients such as baking soda, salt, borax, lemon juice and white vinegar can be put to good use in the kitchen and bathroom. A damp cloth dipped in white vinegar will bring back shine to chrome taps for instance and an equal mixture of borax and baking soda brushed into grout and left for 30 minutes before rinsing will usually remove dark stains.

There is a lovely little book by Angela Martin called *Natural Stain Remover - clean your home without harmful chemicals.*[9] It is full of great ideas you can use around the house to break anyone's dependency on mass-produced cleaning products.

If you need another reason to help you make the switch, read more from Pat Thomas at WDDTY. Type *'Household cleaners- A witch's brew'* into the search engine and steel yourself. I warn you, it is not for the faint-hearted!

I stopped using aerosol sprays of any kind. They can contain **HCFC**s, bad for the planet, as well as the neurotoxic and reproductive toxins **propane, butane** and **isopropane**. Therefore, air fresheners no longer figure as an item I purchase. I make these myself. It is surprisingly easy: I have natural pump action spray glass bottles filled with filtered water and different combinations of essential oils, to sanitise my bathroom and toilet. Tea tree and lavender are great bacteria busters and I have found *The Fragrant Pharmacy* by Valerie Ann Worwood to be a mine of information and recipes for the house.[10]

Recently, I invested in a steam-cleaning machine. It was quite expensive but is a great way to clean and sanitise toilets, walls, carpets most things really, without the use of any cleaning products.

In the garden, I do not use insecticides as they are bad for the environment and for bees and they are, of course, carcinogenic. There is some evidence emerging that childhood leukaemias may be linked to household insecticides[11]. Instead, I have used washing-up liquid, crushed garlic and rosemary to get rid of green fly and aphids. It works, although you need to keep re-applying it often. If there are any flee-ridden pets in the house, combing Neem oil through your pet's coat and spraying a dilution of it on all the surfaces deemed necessary is a much safer option. I am told that this also works to deter ants from invading the kitchen.

Another thing to consider is the impact that a lot of our modern technology is having on our health. For example - daily exposure to **Electromagnetic Fequencies** (EMFs) and **radiation**. My particular type of cancer seems to have exposure to radiation as one of its causes. I wonder whether this cancer is on the increase partly because we are relentlessly bombarded by EMFs. Even as I write this, I have been tied to my computer for weeks. Although I have had it fitted with a special chip to counteract the radiation it emits (I hope) and actually feel a lot clearer headed now after a long spell in front of the computer screen, I cannot guarantee that it actually works. I have taken the same precautions with all our mobile phones and try to use mine as little as possible. Our main landline phone is an old fashioned corded one, which allows us to have long conversations safely.

Television is another feature of our modern everyday life that should also have a chip to counteract its emissions. If we can't do that, at least we can make sure that we sit as far as possible from the screen, at least 1.5 metres, to minimise our exposure to its harmful radiation.

Bedrooms are also full of potential hazards. Too many

of us have a frightening array of plugs and electrical devices (TV, radio, hairdryers, etc.) in the bedroom and the resulting EMFs can have a detrimental effect on the immune system.

When it comes to cooking, your chosen method can also have an impact on your health. Ideally, we should all eat as much raw food as possible in order to maximise our intake of nutrients and vital enzymes, since many are destroyed by heat. This is one reason why juicing vegetables is so wonderful for your health. But as we are talking about EMFs, I personally do not use a microwave oven as this way of cooking not only dramatically alters the nutritional content of food, but also because microwave radiation can leak from the seal around the door and through the glass. It then accumulates in the kitchen itself.

Electric wiring and appliances, overhead power lines, photocopiers, mobile phones and cordless telephones, photocopiers, TVs, tube trains and X-ray machines are among the hundreds of everyday items that are now known to give off high levels of electromagnetic fields.

It is beyond the scope of this little book to examine the risks of each and every one of them. However, I can recommend *'The Powerwatch Handbook' by Alasdair and Jean Philips.* [12]

There is an even more controversial source of potential cellular damage known as energy **'black spots'**. Some of us have apparently been sleeping for years on energy 'black spots' without having any understanding of their potential harmful effects on our health. Rudolph Breuss was well aware of this and even recommended that people, whose houses were built over running water, an apparently huge generator of energy black spots, should move as they could not hope to get better otherwise. I have toyed with the idea of enlisting the help of a dowser to check my house for any such spots and tell me what to do. It is still just a thought.

Oddly enough, cats are 'black spots' seekers and will usually settle on such areas, so if like me, you have such pets, they might be showing you where these areas are located. My cats seem to settle wherever I am, so maybe I am in fact, a huge black spot. That would certainly explain a lot!

On a different note, over the last few years I have also refused to have any new **amalgam fillings** and whenever an old one needs replacing, I have a white composite filling instead. Both Norway and Sweden have banned the use of such fillings. Indeed, much has been written on the toxicity of mercury (check Dr. Mercola's website - where else - for some useful articles) and there are a few holistic dentists in this country who do not use amalgam, some even specialise in their safe removal.

Mercury is also found in some vaccines in the preservative **Thiomersal** (Thimerosal.US). While we are on the subject of vaccination, I have recently been offered the flu vaccine by my local medical practice. After 11 years of being left gloriously alone before the onset of the flu season, I suddenly find myself on the "at risk" list. When I queried this, the receptionist told me that the new computer system was more sensitive and that the lymphoma diagnosis would now be enough to include me on the list of patients who had received "immune suppressant therapy". Obviously, the system is not yet "sensitive" enough to read the treatment received.

In any case, if I really needed help to boost my immune system the last thing I would reach for is a vaccine containing such harmful substances as Formaldehyde, a known carcinogen, antifreeze, and Thiomersal to name but three ingredients present in the flu vaccine. Vegetable cocktails and daily walks have kept me a 'flu-free zone' for many years so I shall follow the good advice the receptionist gave me regarding the letter: "just bin it!" she said.

Even our two cats have not had any more regular vaccinations. I use a homeopathic approach to disease prevention and make sure their nutrition is as close to the one they would have naturally, since it is the best way to keep their immune systems functioning properly. So I give them raw meat with an added powder from a company called Feline Futures. This powder ensures that their natural diet of mice is replicated and keeps them in top form.

So there you have it, this is what I have managed to do so far. I keep reading, learning and making a few more changes as and when appropriate, a little tweaking here and a little fine-tuning there.

Please do not think that I go around obsessing about everything around me. Even though I may have given that impression, I can assure you, it is not so. I know really that the best protection of all is a well-nourished body and a happy, meaningful life.

Here's to it!

"RABBITS DON'T GET LYMPHOMA!"

Part Three

LOOKING BACK

Chapter Thirteen

WHY ME?

IT IS ONLY NOW, after more than ten years, that I ask myself why? Not just why did I get cancer, but why did I get well when others did not?

Then there is the question that has plagued me all through the long days and nights of trying to put my story down on paper - ***why write this book at all?***

When I was wrestling with this frustrating and often excruciating process, I kept asking myself that very question. So much needed to be said and I felt that I was not equal to the task. I was also concerned that my account would be taken the wrong way, as if it was an 'ego trip', a kind of glorification of my own uniqueness.

If you have managed to make it this far, without throwing this book away in disgust at my perceived egocentricity, you may be under the misapprehension that cases like mine must be few and far between. Nothing could be further from the truth - there are hordes of us. The reason why you may not have been aware of us is that we come under the category of 'spontaneous remission' or 'anecdotal evidence'. These dismissive terms are used to lump together wonderful examples of the ability **all** human beings possess to heal their bodies and to recover against all odds.

We are discarded because we are considered irrelevant, or we are viewed condescendingly as exceptions that prove the scientific rule. We become invisible and therefore cause no upset in the statistical evidence, the order of things, or change in the status quo.

Rudolf Breuss came across the full force of this unfortunate, blinkered attitude from the medical establishment when he was trying to get official recognition for his cancer treatment.

'Are 45,000 successful cases nothing,' he lamented, 'There is a big difference between knowledge and science. Science should accordingly search for knowledge.' Indeed, but only knowledge acquired through established procedures, such as double blind tests, seems acceptable.

I don't know about you, but I find that common sense is severely lacking in this approach. Worse still, the potential knowledge gained from the evidence of 45,000 people who were treated successfully is lost forever.

Here lies one of my reasons for writing this book. Stories like mine need to be told because they demonstrate that there are other ways to look at disease and its many causes, other ways to treat it. Stories like mine show that we **all** have the potential to change our established destructive patterns and heal ourselves. They also demonstrate that nutrition cannot be ignored anymore as a means to restore health.

I also hope this book makes you realise that there are many more options available to us than we previously thought regarding the treatment of such life-threatening diseases as cancer.

Talking of hope, I very much hope that this book can play its part in bringing light into the darkness that surrounds this disease. Let it be a ray of hope to all those who, like me, have been told they have cancer.

Let no one discourage you from choosing alternatives to chemotherapy and radiotherapy, even if doctors turn up on your doorstep trying to convince you that you are a fool for doing so and that you will die if you do not accept conventional treatment. Do you think I am joking? Does this seem a little too far-fetched? Well, it isn't. This actually happened to a friend of mine who chose a more holistic approach to the treatment of her particular cancer.

Let no one bully you into doing something that does not feel right to you; give you a poor prognosis or worse, tell you that your time is up. Do not allow any doctor, no matter how much you admire and respect their profession, take away the very thing you need to get your health back. Most doctors do so out of an incomprehensible desire not to give 'false hope' to patients and their families. Hope is what sustains us when everything else falls apart. How can hope be false?

Lawrence LeShan, a brilliant psychotherapist, understood the importance of hope in our lives. He spent many years working with cancer patients and his work led him to understand the context in which cancer developed. He noticed in a large majority of the people he saw that 'there had been, previous to the first noted signs of the cancer, a loss of hope in ever achieving a way of life that would give real and deep satisfaction, that would provide 'a solid raison d'être', the kind of meaning that makes us glad to get out of bed in the morning and glad to go to bed at night.'[13]

Knowing that, in about 80 percent of cancer cases there is already a despair so profound and a blackness so deep as far as the future is concerned, is it not insane then to also remove from us the faint hope of life itself? Does it not make sense, on the other hand, to use the unequalled power of hope to alter the inner environment of your body and return it to a healthy state?

Some enlightened members of the medical profession such as Bernie Siegel, already do this, for they have witnessed many seemingly 'miraculous' recoveries. Here is what he has to say on the matter, in *Peace, Love and Healing*:

'I consider it my job as a doctor to give my patients both (love and hope), because that's what they need to be able to live. Since I don't know what the outcome will be for an individual, no matter what the pathology report says, I can in all honesty give everyone hope... It does not matter what

the disease is. There is always room for hope. I am not going
to die because of statistics. I hope you won't either.'(14)

Bless him and his little cotton socks!

Many books have been written on cancer already, so why add my own? I have read quite a few myself, many by people who were established 'fountains of knowledge' themselves. Doctors such as Max Gerson or nutritionists, or even well established 'gurus' like Deepak Chopra. And then you have Brandon Bays, author of *The Journey*, who seemed so wise and spiritual even before she had cancer. This extraordinary woman obliterated a football-sized tumour in her body in six and a half weeks. She did mention briefly going on a kind of cleansing diet and taking various herbs, but the core of her healing work was done by releasing unexpressed emotions, through the letting go of old hurts, layer by layer in a process she devised herself and which is now being taught in workshops all over the world. Yes, these were inspiring reads indeed, but these people seemed to be in a league of their own. How could an ordinary person ever achieve something so extraordinary?

I guess this is also the reason why I dared to write this account of my recovery, because **I am** an ordinary person and because, in spite of my initial ignorance, I have come to meet first hand the amazing force that inhabits each and every one of us. We need not be powerless when we face this disease.

So as well as a message of hope, I want this book to contain a realisation of your own body's almost magical healing power. No one needs a degree or immense wisdom to access it because it is part of who we are.

This leads me to another difficult question - another why? If our bodies have this amazing ability to heal themselves then **why did I get cancer in the first place?**

Many people talk about genes when trying to find an answer. "It's all in your genetic blueprint" they say, as if we all have little time-bombs within our DNA waiting to explode at a given time, unleashing their destructive power within our cells. For a while, I too subscribed to this gloomy vision of who we are and accepted the limitations that automatically went with it.

On the face of it, cancer had well and truly established itself in my family. Its trail of destruction could be seen through three generations at least, enough evidence that the cancer gene reigned supreme over us. But if that is so, what has happened to my cancer gene in the last 11 years? If my DNA is so irrevocably tainted by the mark of this disease, why am I now free of it?

I asked myself these questions until a few years ago when my friend Denise convinced me to go with her to a really bizarre sounding 'Cancer and Laughter Workshop' in Glasgow. I went partly because I thought that whoever could even think of putting those two words, cancer and laughter, together must be worth meeting in the flesh.

One of the speakers was Dr. David Hamilton, who has so graciously provided the foreword for this book. He was just about to publish his research in the form of a book entitled *It's The Thought That Counts*. He was full of enthusiasm during the workshop, telling us how our thoughts and emotions impact on our cells. According to him you could literally laugh yourself back to health. Among the many anecdotes he recounted, one in particular made a lasting impression on me. It was about a woman diagnosed as schizophrenic who went through an extraordinary physical transformation whenever she changed personality. She did not do so with wigs or make-up, oh no. Somehow, as she became this other person, the colour of her eyes changed.

When I heard this story, something went 'Ping!' inside my head. I had read somewhere (so many books, so many authors, my poor brain can only retain so much) that people who suffered from this multiple personality syndrome did so because they could not allow themselves to express or even feel certain emotions. Somehow they needed to be different people; one personality could not possibly contain the full range of human emotions. This was another defining moment for me. I realised then that strong emotions could indeed switch genes on and off.

Recently, I discovered that there is a field of research called epigenetics.

In the field of epigenetics, (epi means 'above' so the term

translates roughly as 'control above the level of the genes') Dawson Church who wrote the book *The Genie in your Genes* informs us that there are over 100 genes in our bodies which are activated by our thoughts, feelings and experiences. These genes dramatically affect our immune system and our resistance to disease and they can be turned on and off deliberately through thoughts, emotional responses and the experiences that we choose. As a rule, genes require a certain environment to become activated. This environment, according to Church's book is a vast concept and includes both *the inner environment* - the emotional, biochemical, mental, energetic and spiritual landscape of the individual - and *the outer environment*. This outer environment is also multi-facetted and includes 'the social network and ecological systems in which the individual lives. Food, toxins, social rituals and sexual cues are examples of outer environmental influence that affect gene expression.'[15] It would seem that most of our genes respond to signals from the environment.

So, if the cancer gene or oncogene exists and members of my family are, unfortunately, very adept at switching it on, then the transformation of my inner and outer environment since my diagnosis was apparently strong enough and genuine enough to turn it off.

But what could have been so powerful as to switch it on in the first place?

A study conducted over many years by Caroline Beddell Thomas of John Hopkins School of Medicine in the United States examined the relationship between psychological characteristics and disease. She found that cancer patients tended to have had unhappy childhood relationships with their parents and, more importantly perhaps, they reacted by repressing their emotions in the years since.

Much as I hate to admit it, this applies to me.

Don't worry, I am not about to launch into some sort of parent-bashing episode. Part of my recovery has been due to the fact that I stopped blaming my past and the people in it for the way I felt. However, because I learnt early on in my life to repress certain emotions that were either too unbearable to feel, too unacceptable or too awful to express, I became disconnected from my true self. This kind of pressure is relentless and looking back, I can see how this had a bearing on me getting cancer when I did.

From the age of about four, photos show me as a little girl with a permanently puzzled brow and a mouth that does not know whether to laugh or cry. With the benefit of hindsight, I assume that by the time these photos were taken, the strain of having a mother whose emotions were always unpredictable must have taken its toll. Living with my mum was a bit like living with Dr. Jekyll and Mrs Hyde.

My younger brother was born when I was five and the intensity of his bond with her made me think that, for some unknown reason, she had withdrawn her love from me. My older brother then seemed to take on some of the mothering of his little sister and would read me stories at night, for instance. It was he who taught me how to plait my dolls' hair and answered many of the awkward questions that children sometimes ask parents about life, the universe and everything.

To this day, I am still not quite sure how it happened but I got the message early on that I was not good enough to be loved.

Several years of counselling and many soul-searching workshops later, I can see with greater clarity now how the little girl I once was could have felt that way.

My generation suffered greatly from the aftermath of the Second World War. I am one of the 'Baby Boomers', a child of the Fifties born to a generation traumatised by several years of terror and shame. As I was growing up, I remember that the War was mentioned on a daily basis. I also remember that my father was deeply affected by it. His eyes always had the dark shadow of pain in them and a part of him always seemed to be missing or unavailable to us somehow. He talked about the War a great deal and was often told by my mother to stop 'boring us with the same old stories'. One of them struck me as particularly awful.

He had been a prisoner of war for the greater part of the conflict. He escaped many times and was finally held prisoner in a camp at the frontier of Russia. When the war ended, the Russians 'liberated' his camp, or more accurately, they opened the gates and told everyone to make their own way back to France. They offered no help whatsoever in finding a safe route back, even though the ceasefire had not reached certain parts of the country. My dad was one of the last officers remaining in the camp and was therefore in charge of hundreds of soldiers. They came to the edge of a vast, frozen river one night and had no option but to cross it. It was a quiet, moonlit night as the soldiers started their crossing. All was well until suddenly, without warning, the ice broke and silently, the river swallowed up the unfortunate soldiers who were on it. They all died without a sound.

My father's face still looked horror-struck as he recounted this tragic event. Throughout my childhood, even though I did not understand it at all, in those moments, I felt the weight of the burden he was carrying. It deeply shocked me. His pain seemed to suck the very life out of him. It scared me. It took my kind, loving dad away, so far away and made him separate from us, unreachable. It was more than I could bear.

When did I decide that if my mother could not listen to him then I would? When did I sense I had to make him feel better or that I had to be his strength, his support? I don't know, but this is apparently what we do as children, because we depend so completely on our parents for our own survival we take on inappropriate burdens. I became my father's protector. I took on his pain, his guilt at having survived where so many perished and his feeling of not belonging to the world of the living. Being there for him and bringing joy to his life became the sole reason for my existence.

However, I do not want to give the impression that my early life was joyless. My father really doted on me his daughter, his *'rayon de soleil'* his 'sunbeam'. I also had a very funny, very kind and patient older brother whose tolerance I repaid one day by smashing a full jam jar on his head, in a fit of jealous rage. My mother was sometimes the kind of mum I needed, but not for long as Mrs Hyde would appear again suddenly, when I least expected her. The whole household would dread those times when anxiety or rage would render her unrecognisable. When I was 12-years-old I remember asking my dad whether mum loved us on our way to church. By this I really meant to ask him whether she loved **me**. His answer was that of course she did, but she was not well and her illness got in the way. I always felt unconvinced by this explanation since my mum's illness did not seem to get in the way of her love for my younger brother, for instance.

As I grew up, I hid my shattered heart under rebelliousness.

Outside our dysfunctional family unit, relationships were also far from easy. At school, I was so convinced of my own worthlessness that I even invented fictitious members of my family, like a millionaire godfather living in Brazil, to make me seem more interesting to my friends. I sometimes caught myself believing my own lies. Once, I rashly invited one of my school friends to come to Brazil with me one summer. Of course, when the truth inevitably came out, the very thing I had feared the most happened. She was furious with me and promptly wanted nothing more to do with me. Such episodes only served to magnify my feelings that I was definitely unworthy of love.

I tried very hard to be good. I learnt to put other people's needs before my own. I learnt to swallow the resentment I felt when no one seemed to do the same for me. This only demonstrated further that I was not good enough to be loved. So I would try even harder... I am sure you get the picture. Eventually, I became totally disconnected from some of my most unacceptable and painful emotions and, as a consequence, from my own self. I allowed some of my 'dark stuff' to be seen by a trusted few, my best friend Monique was one but even with her, I was not completely honest at times and I kept some of the real me hidden, even from her sight.

This was a dangerous game to play, one that always made me feel insecure about people's affection. Although some appeared to like me, I always felt that if they knew the awful truth about me they would desert me in an instant.

This fear of being abandoned has been the bane of my life!

Something in me never gave up though. I will call this my survival instinct. In my early 20s I realised that, if I wanted to have a chance to live for myself, I had to do it away from my family and away from my 'cosy-but-deadly' bourgeois surroundings. My instincts warned me that I had compromised myself too far already. I felt my despair mounting up. I had to escape before what was left of the real me collapsed altogether under the weight of the burdens I had unwittingly chosen to carry and of the expectations placed on my shoulders.

The message I had received over the years was that *la fille de la maison*, the daughter of the house, had a particular role in the family unit. Daughters, for instance, were brought up to be the ones performing all the household chores. My brothers never lifted a finger around the house. Daughters might go to university if they were intelligent enough, but did not really need to have a career because, first and foremost, they would marry well – a doctor perhaps as per my mother's dream – and have children. Daughters would also look after their ailing parents in their dotage. My dad used to refer to me as *mon bâton de vieillesse*, the prop of his old age, an expression that would send chills of doom down my spine, despite my love for him. He never referred to my brothers in this way.

I had seen first hand the damage such expectations had done to my mother. Part of her emotional fragility must have come from the immense resentment she, a very intelligent woman, harboured within herself at being thus limited in her options.

These preordained plans for my future left much to be

desired. I therefore plotted my escape carefully. Along with my survival instinct came quite a surprising ruthless streak. It made me keep quiet about my intentions until the last minute. I waited until I was 21 years old. In those far off days, you only became of age at 21. By then, parents could not legally stop you from making your own decisions. I knew from past experience that my mum's anxieties ruled the household. Anything that made her feel fretful or anxious required total obliteration at the earliest opportunity. I knew that my plans were of a kind to bring forth Mrs Hyde, so I kept quiet and waited until the end of my English degree. During that last year, I filled in various forms designed to find a school in the United Kingdom which would employ me as a French assistant for a whole year. I ultimately wanted to teach English in France and, before going on to do my post-graduate teaching degree, thought it would be a good idea to spend a year in England, learning first-hand about its culture. The fact that I would also have the opportunity to experience life on my own terms was both thrilling and terrifying.

I knew I had done the right thing when my mother went into a full-blown anxiety attack given the *fait accompli* of my imminent departure. She had one of her 'turns' and, when she saw that it did not have the desired outcome, she tried to scare me with the dangers that I would encounter in a foreign country. She also mentioned again what an ungrateful daughter I was and that, of course, I would be the death of her. However, when she saw not only my resolve but also realised she could do nothing to stop me, she went along with my decision gracefully, in one of her famous U-turns. It was only going to be for a year after all.

As it happens, I met Ian, who was to become my husband that year, so I never went back. No opportunity to remind me of my 'betrayal' has been missed since.

Being away from my family made me face my insecurities. They came to the fore when I realised I was in love with Ian and did not want to lose him. My efforts to put his wishes before my own nearly brought about the very thing I was trying to avoid. Ian announced one day that he did not want to be with a 'puppet', he wanted a real person. From that day on I tried to call back some of the forgotten aspects of my true self. However, I can honestly say that it was not until after I was diagnosed with cancer that I really learnt to accept and express myself fully, **regardless of the consequences**.

In case you're wondering - no, I have not lost track of the question regarding what could have been powerful enough an emotion to switch on the cancer gene. All I have mentioned so far is my way of setting the scene, so to speak. I am sure that the gene would have switched on sooner had it not been for the fact that I still had hope then.

Let me try and explain what I mean. I spent many years

in a profession that was far from ideal for me. Not only do you need self-esteem by the bucketful to be a successful teacher but you need to have passion for your chosen subject too. My passion was for English. However, I compromised and did the logical thing when I decided to stay in England - I taught French instead.

I should have known that teaching French in a country where so many young people thought foreign languages were at best a waste of time, was going to be a very tough assignment indeed. As one of them told me many times when I was trying to get through to him, "Everybody, like, speaks English, innit Miss?" Already, as I studied for my Post Graduate Certificate in Education in London, and more particularly, during my teaching practice at a comprehensive school in Harold Wood near London, I started to feel the strain. Some mornings I could not even face going to my classroom and standing alone in front of all the eager little faces. What's wrong with that? I hear you ask. Well, it was definitely not an eagerness to learn French I could see in front of me, no, it was much more akin to mischief making, unfortunately.

I never felt I measured up. I spent hours preparing my lessons in the vain hope that the material would speak for itself and conceal my perceived abysmal lack of ability for keeping them interested. I hid my fears remarkably well though and even delivered some very good lessons, but inside I was dying.

Even so, the cancer gene did not switch on. I **hoped** that teaching would become easier after a while and, truly, it did. I was still fuelled by the energy of youth and had a strong sense of direction. I wanted to be a teacher. I had invested a lot of years in my studies both in France and in England. A lot of dedication went into proving to everyone that I could be a professional woman, that instead of staying at home 'darning socks' (as per my father's view of the role of women in society), I could have a career and be successful. So much of my self-esteem and self-image were invested in my chosen profession that I could never allow anything to stand in the way. Who was I if not a teacher?

Yet, the stress of the job was relentless, but it was nothing compared to the stress I put myself under trying to play the part of 'She Who Is In Control'. It became more and more difficult to keep my inner mess from coming through and depression set in. Valium became a personal friend of mine for a while and dulled my fears. This only lasted a short while though, as I hated the way it made life an echo of the real thing. My head seemed filled with cotton wool. So one day, I stopped the pills and because I did not have the self-belief required to do battle with unruly children on a daily basis, I stopped teaching for a while too.

The first wave of relief over, I sunk even deeper. I had no idea what to do. I hung around the house like a lost soul. I must have been unbearable to live with.

I worked as a travel courier for a few years. I had been so depressed that, when I saw this job advertised and realised that it entailed travelling to France on a regular basis, I applied. Ian encouraged me. He meant to be supportive and thought that anything was preferable to having me moping around the house, but I saw that as the final nail in the coffin of our relationship. I assumed he could not even bear to be with me anymore. If he loved me, how could he stand being away from me for days on end? Of course, I never told him how I felt. What a missed opportunity to realise that he felt just as lost as I was and did not know how to help me!

We were also trying to start a family and had not had any success. Now, I wonder why? Could it be perhaps that choosing this time to conceive, when I was away in France for a couple of weeks each month, was not really the most suitable of times? Still, my biological clock was ticking. I was in my early 30s and I thought that, despite great reservations about my ability to be a good mother, it was now or never.

Nothing worked. I was put on fertility treatment for 2 years, even though I appeared to be ovulating regularly. I could have carried on but I did not like the thought of my hormones being 'messed about with', so I stopped the treatment. IVF was the next port of call but neither of us felt we could envisage it, so that avenue remained unexplored.

I look back on those years as a time **when my hope**

of ever having a normal, happy and meaningful life started to fade.

That time nearly broke us and, in a final attempt to find answers, we had some counselling. It helped us reconnect with each other and gain some deeper understanding of who we were. In fact, it made all the difference otherwise I think that the gene would have switched itself on right there and then.

When we moved to Scotland 10 years later, many of my unresolved issues came back to haunt me. I felt utterly lost and desolate. The uprooting was so traumatic that it threatened the very foundations of my relationship with Ian. On the plus side, Ian had found a job that seemed to fire his enthusiasm but this was somehow also part of the problem. He was so intent on proving himself worthy of his new position that nothing else seemed to exist. **I** did not seem to exist.

I had not realised until then how much I depended on Ian for **my reason to live**, how much his love meant to me. I felt that as long as he needed me, I had a reason to be. It was a bad time to come to this understanding. I was in a country that was, as yet, unfamiliar to me. Although I now regard it totally as my home and love it with a passion, it felt alien then. I felt uprooted, literally.

My last job in England had been as a teacher of modern

languages in a sixth form college in Colchester. I can truth-fully say that it was the only time I ever felt I enjoyed my work and that I was doing it well. The modern languages department was run by an inspired Scot, a truly gifted teacher. My colleagues were also great characters and we all got on so well! We were such a good team. We had fun together and supported each other. It was a wrench to leave those dear friends behind.

Going from a job that gave me for the first time in my life, a sense of being part of something, a sense of belonging to a group that valued and respected what I had to contribute, but was also so demanding that it took every minute of my weekdays and most of my weekends, to having no structure at all and no identity anymore was a huge shock. Being unemployed for the best part of my first year in this new environment was also more humiliating than I had ever imagined.

Had I considered trying my hand at other occupations, at least for a while, I might have realised sooner that what someone does for a living is not necessarily all that they are. I knew that of course, but I was letting my anxieties about our finances get in the way. Instead of using that year to find out what else I could do with my life, what aspects of me had been lying dormant until then, I spent that time feeling angry at everything and everyone. Not a healthy attitude.

When I eventually found a part-time position in a local school, I should have been brave enough to turn it down.

Instead, I took the position with a heavy heart. I took it to pay the mortgage. I took it because I thought nothing better would come my way. I took it in spite of my survival instinct screaming that I was making a mistake.

I lasted nearly three years during which time I felt more and more redundant as a teacher.

Because I saw nothing better on the horizon, because my diet depended too much on 'diet' drinks laced with aspartame, because I doubted even that Ian and I should stay together, 'click' that little gene started to stir. Because I was older and felt that I was going down towards inevitable decrepitude and death, because I had failed to fulfill the basic role of womanhood by remaining childless, because I was a failure and had come to the end of my usefulness in Ian's life as I saw it, 'buzz' went the oncogene as it got the message that really this woman wanted to die.

I know some of you will think these are the ramblings of a crazy woman and there is not much evidence that thoughts and feelings can have such an impact on health. Well, let me quote Dr. Hamilton again:

> 'In reality, our intentional and unintentional visualisations inspire DNA twenty-four hours a day, three hundred and sixty five days a year... we continually affect our genetic code and the nature of the effect is simply down to the nature of our thoughts, feelings, attitudes, beliefs, and intentions.'[16]

So you see, I am not making all this up.

Quite possibly, all my thoughts of doom and gloom caused a build up of diseased cells in my body way before, finally, the cancer gene turned itself on. Somehow there is wisdom even in this, as I see it. Nature always gives you a chance to reverse the process. A bit of counselling here, a better diet there and a sunnier attitude will all start to reverse the disease process and create healthier cells.

A gross oversimplification I know and yet even if, like me, you get so far down the road to disease and develop one that is life-threatening, even then you may still reverse the process.

There have been some real miracles, where a cancer disappeared overnight, the so-called 'spontaneous remissions'. Some theories credit another gene, the interleukin-2 gene which can cause the immune system to neutralise cancer cells, for such miracles. But what triggers this 'miracle gene'? According to Dr. Hamilton '…tremendous faith, hope, determination, visualisation, a complete change of belief system, or some powerful experience.'[16]

Although my own recovery did not happen overnight, it took place nonetheless and quite against the expectations of many. The best I could have hoped for, had I accepted chemotherapy, radiotherapy or both, would have been a period of remission followed by more treatment and so on, for the rest of my life. I never asked what my consultant meant by that, the rest of my life. Probably just as well.

I do remember however speaking to another oncologist about my unexpected progress, on the rare occasion when Dr. Clarke had not been available. He confirmed that I was doing very well indeed, but when I tried to be funny and joked that it was "Carrots that Cured my Cancer" he was not amused. He even warned me that I would have a very tough time proving that what I did had any impact on my cancer.

Well, this is not about proving anything to anyone. This is about letting you all know that there are other options you might want to consider before deciding whether you go down the conventional route.

This is about telling the truth.

Chapter Fourteen

WHAT CAUSED MY CANCER TO DISAPPEAR?

What caused my cancer to disappear?

OVER THE PAST TEN YEARS or so, I have often wondered why I became well again when others, who also made changes to their diet and who apparently had the same desire to 'beat' their cancer, did not? I was particularly shocked when I heard that Barry Sheene, a rather dashing motorbike racer who had survived many crashes in the seventies and eighties, had died of cancer. He had refused chemotherapy and was using the Breuss diet. I felt sure he would recover, so why didn't he?

The frustrating thing for someone like me who wants to 'save' everyone is that I will never know. The path that leads to disease is unique for each individual and likewise, the journey back to health. The only thing I can attempt to do as far as I am able to, is shed some light on what made **my** recovery possible.

I might be tempted to try a flippant: "Well, it was easy. I did not have chemotherapy or radiotherapy!" Very tempting indeed, especially when you know that chemotherapy, for instance, does **not** cure 96 to 98% of all cancers.

No, I have not picked this percentage out of thin air, if that's what you are thinking. Recently, a book written by Andreas Moritz fell into my eager little hands. The title itself is quite a challenge to established views on this disease: *Cancer is not a disease, it's a survival mechanism.* In this profound, impressively well-researched study, Andreas Moritz mentions the work of Dr. Ulrich Abel from the Tumour Clinic of the University of Heidelberg. After years spent collecting and evaluating data regarding the use of chemotherapy as a treatment for cancer, the conclusion Dr. Abel came to was that the overall success rate of chemotherapy was 'appalling' and that there was no evidence chemotherapy can 'extend in any appreciable way the lives of patients suffering from the most common organic cancers.' *('Chemotherapy of Advanced Epithelial Cancer: a critical review', Biomedicine and Pharmacotherapy, 1992; 46: 439-452.)*[17]

Furthermore there is some evidence that people who receive no treatment can go into remission, or self-induced healing as I much prefer to call it. In fact, the oncologist I mentioned in the previous chapter had offered this evidence as a way to mock my belief in the "Healing Power of Carrots". Some people, especially those who are quite elderly receive no treatment for their cancer, he said. They could not survive it, he said (no argument from me there) and quite a few recover **without doing anything at all**, he said.

Well, I wondered if anyone had bothered asking these people whether they had indeed 'done nothing' or whether they had in fact made a few crucial changes to their diet, for instance, or some other aspect of their life or their approach to it? He had no idea. Most people disappeared once they got better.

It was Ian who asked the most probing question:

"How do you know that more people would not recover in this way? You treat everyone, that's the problem!"

According to Andreas Moritz there is no contest, among cancer patients, those who receive no conventional cancer treatment have 'an up to four times higher remission rate' than those who do. So it could be that first and foremost, my lack of conventional treatment played a big part in my recovery.

Yet it's not as simple as that. Against my better judgement, I have to admit that in a few instances these barbaric ways of trying to eradicate cancerous tumours seem to have some success, or are part of something that works, for a particular individual.

A friend who was also diagnosed with a form of non-Hodgkin's lymphoma a year or so before me, was treated with chemotherapy. He totally embraced this kind of treatment. He received more conventional treatment to remove a secondary cancer on his spine some time later and had injections of interferon for a year, as part of a trial. He recovered. Of course, he also made changes to his diet and certain aspects of his life. He also started to have reflexology on a weekly basis when his treatment ended. Was this enough to make a difference?

To quote Bernie Siegel again, 'Anything that offers hope has the potential to heal.'[18] Perhaps we tend to give too much credit to the method used when in fact it is the **power of belief** that really causes a person to heal. Bernie Siegel himself admits that the only reason he still works as a surgeon is because, for some people, surgery is an absolutely necessary step in their recovery. It is their 'magic bullet', the key that unlocks their healing potential.

I am totally prepared to admit that, in my case also, my belief in what I was doing was one of the reasons I regained my health. I read that this kind of approach had worked for countless others and that knowledge gave me hope. My poor prognosis regarding chemotherapy's impact on my type of lymphoma also motivated me in finding an alternative that would not involve having chemotherapy throughout the rest of my life. Carolyne Myss puts it thus:

'The heart holds the catalyst that causes the rest of the bodymind to heal in a chain reaction.'[19] My own heart became joyfully and completely engaged in my chosen approach. I didn't waste a second doubting that juicing organic vegetables would work or thinking that my visualisations might be futile. I embraced this new approach to living with an energy, a passion I should have had earlier. Well, it's never too late to learn!

Other than this total belief in what you are doing to heal yourself it would seem that **personality** might also play a part in achieving a successful outcome. It would seem that those patients who recover are more often than not those who **take an active part** in their recovery, those who ask awkward questions.

I got well, therefore, partly because once I recovered from the shock of the diagnosis, I became involved in finding a way to make it happen, instead of "leaving it all to the doctors because they know best" as so many people told me they would have done, had they been in my shoes. Dr. Clarke herself was aware that not being an 'ideal patient' was a good sign, as far as my prognosis was concerned. She told Ian that the patients who did best were the 'awkward ones', and the ones who did least well were those who 'just took the medicine'. So it seems that rediscovering my fighting spirit as well as my talent for being a 'pain in the backside' helped me recover my health. What a refreshing and encouraging way of looking at my stubbornness and my desire to control everything!

Before I had cancer, I had been striving for so long to be 'acceptable' that I had forgotten this aspect of me. Yet as a very young child, I had been willful and difficult, according to my mother.

As a toddler, once I had decided to do something it was virtually impossible to stop me. I had also been fearless and drawn to others much like metal is to a magnet. So in the summer, while my parents were trying to relax on the beach, I would take any opportunity to wander away from the safe perimeter around our tent, to find other people to play with. My poor parents even had to invest in a special, rather cute straw hat with a red pompom on the top, so they could spot me more easily. Finding me gone, they would frantically search for me all over the beach, fearing the worst, and would inevitably spot me sitting on some stranger's knees, eating biscuits and happily chatting away. Instead of being angry with me they should have thanked me, for they made good friends through my escapades.

It is possible therefore that I got my health back because, from the moment I realised I was not quite the failure I thought I was, almost as if a switch had been thrown, I became that little fearless Shirley Temple clone again. Gone were my insecurities. I had one simple choice to make: to live or to die. I chose to live and having at last made that choice, **little Cathie reminded me of who I was** before I suppressed my true self. Because I needed all my energy to regain my health, I could no longer use it to keep myself hidden. I let myself be. I realised that all those years, **I** was the one who had kept me under lock and key. Because this energy was released, my body could then use it to heal itself.

Louise Hay writes in her book, *The Power is Within You*, that she also believes we contribute towards the creation of every condition in our lives, good or bad, with our thinking, feeling patterns. Likewise, **I knew that I had played a part in my getting cancer, and through this acceptance came the power to put things right**.

By this I do not mean that I willingly gave myself cancer and that it was therefore my fault I became ill. I only mean that I was unaware of the impact my repressed thoughts and emotions had on my health until I became aware of the role they had played in my getting cancer. Far from making me feel guilty for having somehow been responsible for my illness, it simply opened my eyes to the power thoughts and emotions have on our health and happiness.

It also gave me a key to **using this power consciously** to heal my body. Louise Hay's affirmations helped me alter my thoughts and change the way I felt about myself and the way I lived my life. Quite literally, those affirmations initiated a process of transformation so great that it obliterated my negative patterns. It was almost as if all of a sudden, I had become that intrepid little girl on the beach again; as if all those years of doubt and fear in between had never existed.

When I look back at the years before my cancer, I see a person who was not really living her life and I want to shake her until she gets some sense back into herself! Well, I guess cancer gave me a timely reminder that this life is finite and that my time was running out. I think that I did in fact get the shaking I so badly needed.

Cancer gave me the ultimate choice to make, the choice between life and death. To really choose life, I had to find out what I really wanted to do with it. Because I looked death in the eye, I lost my fear of living.

Until then, I had only lived half a life, never connecting fully with it, always fearful of being hurt and rejected. Well, enough, no more! Suddenly, I wanted to know what it was like to live a meaningful life before I died, whenever that was going to be. Many of the changes I made were due to this realisation and, you know, those long overdue changes were easy to make once I refocused my energy on living and being myself, regardless of the consequences.

In that process **I rediscovered my intuition**, my 'inner guidance' in Louise Hay's words. She explains that it is important to get in touch with it 'because it is the wisdom that knows the answers for you' [20]. That wisdom or 'inner ding' as she calls it had led me to reflexology. Yes, even in those days where I was so cut off from myself, I still had moments of inspiration and courage. I sensed that it could be a fascinating field to study and practise. I knew that it was my kind of thing even though I had never experienced it. Much later on, when my intuition (and Graham's warning) let me know that somehow chemotherapy was not for me, I listened.

A certain form of ruthlessness or as I prefer to call it, a **self-focus**, was required to put all these changes into action and I re-discovered this 'gift' with stupefying ease. I became utterly aware of the people whose energy was beneficial to me and also of those who drained my own. Amazingly for the 'people pleaser' I had become, **I learnt to say NO**. Not that I became unkind, far from it, but I was aware that all my energy was needed for this healing to occur. I could not afford to allow anyone to make me doubt that what I was doing was right, or to make unreasonable demands on my time.

This new attitude cost me a few friends. But it also brought many blessings in my life. It brought me new friends and, with them, more support and love than I ever expected to find.

Surprisingly, it did not make Ian run away.

His support in all this is one of the major reasons why I was able to get my health back. He made my juices when he was home, ate the same food as I did and went to every hospital appointment with me. Rather touchingly, he kept his fear from me. We developed a new understanding and a new respect for each other. We even grew closer as a result of this newfound honesty of mine. "But of course", I hear all you wise ones say.

Even my mother surprised me when she told me she supported my chosen way of dealing with my disease. I admit I had expected her to try and persuade me to have chemotherapy instead of buying carrots by the truckload. I expected her to listen to her own fears first and foremost. But no, once again I had misjudged her. What she said was that I sounded as though I knew what I was doing. I have kept a little note she sent me early on, with a cheque to buy some organic food. It starts with these words *'Pour notre fille chérie'* (To our darling daughter). I owe a great part of my recovery to that little note. It said what I had longed to know for certain all my life. **It told me she loved me** and, for this reason, it still moves me to tears.

It has been a challenging journey for me to let go of my pain, to find my mother again, to accept her and to love her as she is. I know I have been as much of a challenge for her. But somehow, because cancer reminded me that I was mortal, I was able to **stop blaming her and indeed myself** for not being good enough. It seemed crazy to remain frozen in my pain when I needed to let go of it, free myself from its familiar grip in order to live my life with a new, truer purpose. It suddenly seemed so petty, so absurd to invest so much of me in negativity.

How extraordinary that my disease was somehow instrumental in my learning how to **let go of resentment** and how to **forgive**!

It is even more extraordinary when you know what a huge capacity I had for storing resentment until it choked the life out of me, well, nearly did. Cancer gave me an incentive to release the hurts and frustrations I had been nursing over many, many years. I forgave those who had caused me pain not because I suddenly became a benevolent 'Saint Catherine', oh no. My forgiveness was a gift bestowed not

on others so much as upon myself. I needed to stop tortur-
ing myself with past hurts quite simply because holding on
to the past was making me a prisoner of it. To heal, to live,
I needed to be free. As you can imagine, it was a massive
release of energy that suddenly became available for repair
work on all levels. My wise body made good use of it.

That time also taught me how to **be brave and follow
my heart**. For many years, I lost the link with my spirit, my
soul and little by little, my connection to the purpose of
my life. I believe this loss lay at the root of my developing
a life-threatening illness. Mona Lisa Schulz, whose book
literally fell off a shelf as I was browsing through the Mind
Body and Spirit section of Borders, wrote in *Awakening
Intuition*:

> '*The failure to connect with our purpose affects us in the
> seventh emotional center... Critical disease is a message we
> need to receive so that we can re-evaluate some aspect of our
> lives and, most probably, change it.*' [21]

I thought that the purpose of my life had always been to
teach. I clung to this certainty with all the stubbornness I
could muster. Even after I realised that teaching French was
the wrong occupation for me, I still could not see what
could replace this vocation.

Well, sometimes life, God, the Universe, whatever you

care to call it, has a way of taking away the very thing you have become too attached to, forcing you, or rather giving you a chance to 'dig deeper' and find out more about your true self. I eventually got the message but for a while, I felt as if my life was devoid of purpose. Then, my heart was drawn to reflexology, giving me a hint about what I could devote my life to next. Just before the darkness then, there was the faint light of renewed hope. I kept it in my sight on my journey back to health and it has since taken me on a voyage of discovery that seems endless and full of many unexpected blessings.

This whole episode has made me realise that **I need not try and control everything in my life**, that I could simply let life take me where I needed to go.

What a novel experience for the left-brained control freak I was until then!

Many people who survive a disease such as cancer suddenly 'get God' as the saying goes. They understand all at once that a life without spirituality is very incomplete. They know without the shadow of a doubt that we all have a soul and that this part of us is immortal. Well, God and I parted company a long time ago when, as an adolescent growing up in France, I could no longer reconcile the notion that a kind God would allow so much suffering, so much injustice in the world. The opulence of Catholic churches further drove me away from Sunday mass. I decided, along with Karl Marx, that religion was indeed 'the opium of the people'. As a result I closed my heart and ignored the stirrings of my soul.

Yet, as a little girl, I had talked to God as though to a friend, I had sensed his presence in my life and in my heart. After confessing my sins before my first communion, I felt so incredibly light and joyful. Honestly, I thought I had wings!

That a potentially fatal disease could somehow be the key that would open my heart again and free my soul contains a bittersweet irony that is not lost on me.

As I meditated twice a day with the intention of kick starting my immune system, I experienced the wonder of 'going beyond', an outcome I had read a meditative state could achieve. This is the level where, as Deepak Chopra puts it 'silence, the absence of thoughts, emotions, drives, wishes, fears, anything at all, reigns supreme.' [18] In those moments, I felt connected to something immensely powerful and compelling, something that let me know there was nothing for me to fear.

Moments like these instilled such calm within me that I was able to hear the still, little voice of my intuition. It had been lost to me for so long. And my intuition brought me back to my soul. Gary Zukav has a beautiful way of explaining how this connection can be made. He writes in *The Seat of the Soul*:

'Intuition... is the meaning that takes form in the fog of confusion. It is the Light that comes to the darkness. It is the presence of the Divine. Intuition can be thought of as a type of wiring that can be used by various sources, one of these is the soul.' (22)

I do not want you to think that my life has become really easy, or that I have become this amazingly balanced, almost saintly human being. Not a chance! I am very much a work in progress, like most of us. There are still too many occasions when I stumble, when my emotions become confused, when I realise I am more fragile than I thought and that I can still get hurt far too easily. There are other more unsettling times, when I feel that the fire of my anger could incinerate those who have fanned it. The difference is that I do not hide from those emotions any more. I acknowledge them and genuinely do my best to learn from them and let them go.

Life is indeed a journey and its challenges never cease. I try to learn from or just simply accept, these often painful trials and tribulations. I may become angry at the seemingly unfair nature of some of these experiences, but sooner or later, usually later, I understand the lesson I am being given through them.

Now and again the urge to learn new skills and discover new ways to help myself and others be whole comes upon me. I do not fight this, as I know now that the purpose of my life is to be of service to others. It has so far taken me to different forms of reflexology, counselling, Reiki and natural nutrition. What is next for me? Something called PSYCH-K perhaps. This method helps people undo self-limiting beliefs by erasing hidden messages from their subconscious minds. It uses a form of muscle testing very similar to that of Kinesiology and my heart seems drawn to it. We shall see…

No matter what happens in my life, I now feel connected to every aspect of me as never before. 'Little fearless Cathie' is a cherished part of me these days. In the words of Lawrence LeShan, she helps me 'sing my song', be all that I can be.

When I look back on the last 11 years of my life, I feel as though a lifetime of learning has taken place. I also feel that I have been set free from self-imposed captivity.

Cancer was a wake-up call I could not ignore. It taught me more than I could ever hope to learn about myself, about us all. Through this experience, I realised that my body was never my enemy. Of course, at first, I felt it had let me down by allowing cancer, this alien, to take hold of me. But soon, as my fear started to dissipate, I understood that my body had actualy supported me for as long as it could.

There can be no greater stress, no greater strain on the body than not daring to be who you are. Yet, through all the years of repressing my true nature, through all my desperate attempts at snatching little scraps of love here and there, my body kept going. Through all the wrong turns I took, through all the sweet comfort food I ate, my body supported me.

It gave me plenty of signals that things were not right, but I did not understand that migraines, for instance, were a sign that my liver was not coping, or that depression was a warning that already, my toxicity levels had become dangerously high. On another level, they signified that my anger and my despair had also become a threat to my very survival. I did not listen; I did not know my body's language. It took cancer to make me stop going further down the path of self-destruction.

So yes, I dare to say it: cancer was a blessing in disguise, an opportunity to experience first hand how miraculous our bodies are. It was the kind of friend that momentarily comes into your life, when you have something of such magnitude to accomplish that your legs buckle under at the mere thought of it. These friends either bring much needed support or, on the contrary, shake you to your core and force you to reassess who you are and what you believe in.

In truth, cancer brought me back from the dark, from the depth of my inner despair. In that way, my story is not so much the story of a person who found a cure for her disease, but more of a life that was healed.

I would not be who I am today without
this experience because you see, in a most
unexpected way, it was the making of me.
It was my salvation.

CANCER SET ME FREE

"RABBITS DON'T GET LYMPHOMA!"

NOTES TO REFERENCES
IN THE TEXT

Dedication

(1) *Sayings and Tales of Zen Buddhism. Reflections for Every Day* by William Wray. Published by Arcturus.

Chapter Five

(2) *You Can Heal Your Life* by Louise Hay. Copyright 1984, 1987. Published by Eden Grove Editions. Reprinted by permission of The Random House Ltd.

Chapter Six

(3) *Why People Don't Heal and How They Can* by Caroline Myss. Published by Bantam Book. Reprinted by permission of the Random House Group Ltd.

(4) *Peace, Love and Healing* by Bernie Siegel, M.D. Published by Harper Perennial, a division of Harper Collins Publishers.

Chapter Seven

(5) *The Complete Cancer Cleanse.* By Cherie Calbom, John Calbom and Michael Mahaffey. Published by Nelson Books.

Chapter Nine

(6) *Advice for the prevention and natural treatment of numerous diseases, CANCER, Leukaemia and other seemingly incurable diseases* by Rudof Breuss. Published by Walter Margreiter publishers.

Chapter Twelve

(7) *Take Control of Your Health* by Dr. Joseph Mercola with Kendra Pearsall. Published by Mercola.com.

(8) *Cleaning Yourself to Death. How Safe is Your Home?* by Pat Thomas. Published by Newleaf, an imprint of Gill and Macmillan Ltd.

(9) *Natural Stain Remover. Clean Your Home Without Harmful Chemicals.* Published by Apple Press.

(10) *The Fragrant Pharmacy* by Ann Worwood. Published by Bantam Books.

(11) *Household Insecticides.* http://www.NaturalNews.com/027061_pesticides_cancer_NaturalNews.html

(12) *The Power Watch Handbook. Simple ways to make you and your family safer* by Alasdair and Jean Philips. Published by Piatkus.

Chapter Thirteen

(13) *Cancer as a Turning Point* by Lawrence LeShan. Published by Gateway Books.

(14) *Peace, Love and Healing* by Bernie Siegel, M.D. Published by Harper Perennial, a division of Harper Collins Publishers.

(15) *The Genie in Your Genes. Epigenetic Medicine and the New Biology of Intention* by Dawson Church. Published by Cygnus Books by arrangement with Energy Psychology Press.

(16) *How Your Mind Can Heal Your Body* by David R. Hamilton PhD. Published by Hay House UK.

Chapter Fourteen

(17) *Cancer is not a Disease, it's a Survival Mechanism. Discover cancer's hidden purpose, heal its root causes and be healthier than ever* by Andreas Moritz. Published by Cygnus Books. Original edition published by Ener-chi Wellness Press.

(18) *Peace, Love and Healing* by Bernie Siegel, M.D. Published by Harper Perennial, a division of Harper Collins Publishers.

(19) *Why people don't heal and how they can* by Caroline Myss. Published by Bantam Books. Reprinted by permission of the Random House Group Ltd.

(20) *The Power is Within You* by Louise Hay. Copyright 1991. Eden Grove publishers and now Hay House, inc. Carlsbad, CA.

(21) from *Awakening Intuition* by Mona Lisa Schulz. Published by Bantam Books. Reprinted by permission of The Random House Ltd.

(22) from *The Seat of the Soul* by Gary Zukav, published by Rider. Reprinted by permission of The Random House Group Ltd.